A RACING CYCLIST'S
WORST NIGHTMARE

A RACING CYCLIST'S
WORST NIGHTMARE

and

Other Stories from the Golden Age

Tony Hewson

A Racing Cyclist's
Worst Nightmare

First published in 2009 by:
Mousehold Press
Victoria Cottage
Constitution Opening
Norwich
NR3 4BD

www.mousehold-press.co.uk

ISBN 978 1 874739 53 1

Cover design: James Norris

Printed by Barnwells, Aylsham

To all those who care for the past and future of British road racing and especially the boys of the BLRC.

CONTENTS

Author's acknowledgements:
I would like to express my thanks to the following for the help
they have given me:
Nev Barrett, John Dennis, Trevor Fenwick, Tricia Holloway,
Les Lowe, Tom Mayfield, Peter MacFarlane, Dave Orford,
John Pound, Ken Russell, Peter Ryalls, Don Sanderson, John
Scott, Ted Wren and the late Ray Minovi.

Photo credits:
Photosport International (pp 29, 167); Robin Walker (p.40);
Patricia Holloway (pp. 48, 52, 53, 60).
All others fom the author's collection.

Publisher's note:
This year marks our tenth anniversary as a publisher of books
about cycle racing. In a market dominated by two or three huge
organisations the survival of a small publisher is not easy, but
we have managed it. In no insignificant measure this is due to
all the help we have received from numerous people over these
years, and to the encouragement that has come from those
cycling enthusiasts who have telephoned us to place an order
and ended up reminiscing for an hour about the sport and
urging us to 'keep up the good work'. To all of those we give
heartfelt thanks. In particular we must mention Richard Allchin
and his colleague Mike Clark at Sport & Publicity, with whom
we have collaborated on many of our publications. Between us
we have introduced readers to some excellent new writers, and
we have published books of genuine quality which, in a world
where the bottom line is usually the only line, would otherwise
never have seen the light of day.

The author in the Sheffield RCC Mountain Time Trial, April 1951

THE FABULOUS ELSECAR CYCLING CLUB

Sheffield had its posh side and its 'common', its Beverley Hills and its fish and chip shop north. The south bordered the beautiful Derbyshire Dales where well-heeled homeowners lived in luxury and the sun was bribed to shine upon them – or so folklore had it. Wry, plebeian folklore also had it that the purpose of The Great Wall Of Council Estates, where I lived, wasn't really to re-house slum-dwellers but to shield those milksop southerners from winter's Arctic blasts. Joking apart, though, it wasn't a bad place in which to be raised (as hard-man politician David Blunkett will testify). The spacious houses with their large well-tended gardens, the wide roads and avenues, their verges adorned with cock-a-leg trees for canine relief, and everywhere that ruddy-orange glow of tiles and brickwork as though the whole estate wore the perky smile of a Santa Claus granddad. Labour in politics, yet conservative in outlook, this respectable working class community defined crime as 'having fancy ideas' and 'getting too big for thy bloody boots.' No wonder clever-dick Dave in the fullness of time flitted south.

Our house was situated on a wide T-junction, forming a natural arena for neighbouring children and youths to gather. Most parents were young and fruitful, their offspring in plentiful supply, and there was little motor traffic to disturb the skipping and ball games and every sort of imaginative cops 'n robbers play that went on from dawn to dusk in the school holidays outside our front windows When not participating myself, I held a ringside seat. A certain amount of bullying and 'slagging off' accompanied the play. Real 'feights' were rare but when they occurred it was inside a ring of spectators who imposed Marques of Queensbury boxing rules on the contestants: no head-butting, kicking, scratching or pulling of hair – all considered to be cissy and unworthy of the manly arts of battle. Apart from schoolteachers, adults rarely intervened: by common consent, youngsters were expected to stick up for themselves. But let some 'miserable old fogey's' vegetable patch be trampled in search of a lost ball and it was, 'Ah shall tell thi dad when he comes home from work and thou'll be for coppit.' Coppit meant a clip round the ear-hole or worse. Parental responsibility generally operated not in favour of the child, but the community. There might be little in the way of childhood human rights or social services or state handouts, but neither were there knives, guns or drugs. And unlike today, everybody I knew had a mum and dad and every dad worked for a living.

From an early age I loved to watch the bicycle riders circling the arena. They had purpose but no destination. They were simply there to show themselves off and act as ribald monitors of the play. Round and round they rode, a couple of haughty feet above the common herd, interjecting here a taunt, there an insult, only to dart off out of range of skipping-rope retribution then circle back like troublesome wasps. Their manoeuvrability gave them the edge. They accelerated, ducked and dodged like matadors. How I yearned to join them. But every plea to be bought a bike drew the same anodyne response from my parents: 'We shall have to wait and see.' Wait for what, I wondered? That was never made clear.

In fact, I had to wait until I was thirteen when my cycling brother was demobbed from the RAF and put in a good word on my account. One day, to my delight, my dad rolled up wheeling a bike. It was second-hand and had cost him the princely sum of five bob, a big chunk from his small wage packet. It was a Dunelt (a sideline manufacture of the Sheffield tubing and motorcycle firm Dunford and Elliott), black in colour with a sprung, fabric saddle, Sturmey Archer 3-speed hub gear and semi-drop handlebars. I was thrilled. Not so my connoisseur brother who condemned it on sight as a load of old rubbish and 'miles out of track'. He put it to the test by running it through a puddle of water and producing the wet imprint of two parallel tramlines where there should have been only one. The cheap, flexi-tube frame was twisted out of true from what he called in RAF slang 'a prang'. Being out-of-line, the wheels pointed at slightly different compass points, creating drag, and each pedal push wasted energy, like treading across a Bouncy Castle. It was not only pre-war but in his estimation had been through the wars with some previous owner.

This was something I really didn't need to know. Never mind, it was a bike and it belonged to me and as far as I was concerned that was all that really mattered. The problem was I couldn't ride it. I'd never learned how to and this was a matter of some embarrassment because all the other local lads of my age had mastered the art long since, invisibly, as if by osmosis or a gift endowed by nature at birth. And I'd resisted gang elders' offers to 'have a go on my bike, kid', the uncharitable twinkle in their eyes suggesting a concealed motive to make a fool of me in public.

However, having purchased me a duff bike, my dad now set out to redeem himself by teaching me to ride. First it had to be made to fit – it was an adult machine and far too big for me, even with the saddle squashed to the crossbar. He cut four thick pieces of wood and bolted them to the pedals enabling my feet at full stretch to make contact. 'You'll grow into it,' he assured. Then he tied a stout stick beneath the saddle so that it obtruded backwards to serve as a handle.

It was a warm summer's evening and the street was full of my larking teenage mates. I had no desire to make an exhibition of myself in front of them and become the butt of jokes for months on end, so it seemed prudent to walk the bike out of the immediate neighbourhood to somewhere I was incognito. Here my dad helped me mount and holding the stick kept me in balance as he jogged along beside. At first I zigzagged crazily before managing to steer a straight course. I could hear his old, creased boots slapping the tarmac as he ran. I was concentrating so hard that only when the sound of his boots receded did I realise I was riding unaided. A miracle! To keep balance by instinctive minute adjustments of steering – in how many other ways do we so outrageously defy the enormous forces of gravity?

Those firsts, how we remember them – first day at school, first kiss, first cycle ride. Sometimes the trigger for memory is a single detail – the school corridor buffed to a gleam, the waxy taste of lipstick. Here it was my father's sky-blue shirt dark-stained with sweat that for me will forever delineate that moment. I had managed to stop and dismount, but only by letting the bike fall and doing a clumsy sort of skip, skinning an ankle in the process. Then I turned, and there he was jogging towards me in his sweat-stained shirt. My eye clicked and then clicked again as he crouched, veined hands on knees, gasping for breath. He was 57 years old, little exercised by his sedentary job and out of sorts, but on my behalf he had just run for a mile or more. At the time it made little impression. Surely that was what fathers were for, to be there to help their children in the hour of need? But now I think and wonder.

At first, the Dunelt served a mainly utilitarian purpose. I cycled the five miles return trip to school, saving on bus fares. I ran errands for my mother. I used the bike as a packhorse to ferry bats, pads and stumps to nearby Concord Park where we played impromptu cricket matches against kids from other neighbourhoods whom two years ago we'd fought in pitched battles. Then came the day of my first real bike ride. And it was to change my life.

11

It was early afternoon during the school summer holidays and our gang was gathered under the street lamp opposite my house somewhat at a loss for occupation. It was too hot for games, almost too hot for anything except aimless chatter and telling mucky jokes. Tecker had just managed to set a newspaper alight by concentrating the sun's rays through his magnifying glass and was busy kicking the blazing embers in our direction, when Jud emerged from his front gate shoving his bike and announcing he was going to visit his auntie in Elsecar, a mining village some six miles to the north. Did anyone want to join him?

Jud was a bit older than the rest of us and held in great respect on account of his strutting about in a naval cadet's uniform. He was almost an adult, whilst we were still classed as kids. We all put our hands up and grunted assent.

'Right,' he said, 'we've got enough here for a club. All we need now is a name. We're going to Elsecar, right? So let's call it the Elsecar Cycling Club, just to be a bit different.'

I immediately perceived the error in his logic. Calling a cycling club after the destination rather than its place of origin would involve frequent changes of name. It was barmy, but I kept my mouth shut. We'd cross that bridge when we came to it and, anyway, Jud wasn't to be argued with, his word being law.

Within minutes we'd dispersed and reassembled with our bikes, eager to make a start. My Dunelt turned out to the most roadworthy of the ramshackle collection of wrecks assembled beside the lamppost; that is until the last-second appearance of Rupert on his brand new sports cycle.

A word about Rupert: he was one of those kids who never quite gains acceptance and is doomed to hover on the gang's fringes, forever knocking at the door and being repulsed. He was pale, thin and physically weak, a typical 'laddy-lass', often in tears and born to be bullied. Compassion for him was in short supply on account of his genius for 'sticking his oar in where it wasn't wanted'. And then there was his dad. He was reputed to be a spiv, who'd somehow dodged war service. Our fathers' occupations were all orthodox. We knew exactly how each earned his brass – steelworker, miner, tram driver, clerk – but his dad remained a mystery, whilst yet furnishing a life-style a cut above everyone else's. Even under the exquisite torture of the Indian burn, tearful Rupert refused to disclose what it was. Naturally, rumours abounded, including that he'd once been a well-paid Nazi spy – you couldn't get lower than that, though truth to tell, anyone displaying trappings of wealth in our relatively impoverished community was bound to attract suspicion and hostility. The only motorcar in the neighbourhood belonged to Rupert's dad, a Sunbeam-Talbot, its exclusive, creamy paintwork adding insult when black was the pre-dominant 'choice' of the masses. Despite petrol rationing, it could be seen cruising the streets in a brazen parade of social and material superiority. Rupert's clothes and toys were of the best and with his apparently inexhaustible supply of sweets ('spice') he bribed his way into our activities. Unsurprisingly, one of his more printable nicknames was 'Sunbeam'.

Rupert – Sunbeam – was the only one of us this particular day who'd bothered to tell his mother where he was going. He had a neat package of sandwiches in his polished leather saddlebag and money jingled in his pocket. The rest of us snatched whatever we could from the kitchen whilst our mother's back was turned.

Sucking Rupert's mint imperials, we set off downhill, heading north towards Chapeltown, a motley crew in stained shirts and trousers clipped or tied at the ankles above football-scuffed boots or exploding plimsolls. Bomber's bike had no brakes, so to slow down he dropped onto the crossbar and skidded his steel-heeled clogs over the road, giving off a spectacular display of sparks like the tail of a comet.

What little traffic there was mainly consisted of slow, heavily laden lorries that lurched and ground up behind, hooted their wrath and passed in a dust-devil of smoke. This did nothing to deter our wilder element. The novelty of the cycling trip soon wore thin and they amused themselves by weaving around the catseyes and conducting a spitting duel.

Wisely, Sunbeam kept his distance until, passing through the streets of Chapeltown, he uttered a loud cry and stopped. We circled back and found him astraddle his machine, pointing at the front tyre. It was hissing mournfully. A nail protruded through the white wall and had already scored the paintwork inside the fork.

He began to blub. 'Mi bike! Mi dad'll kill me!'

Commiseration was offered: 'Shurrup, daft bugger! Serves thee reight for showin' off.'

Jud's naval training impelled him to take charge of this emergency. He removed wheel from forks and pulled out the nail. His request for a puncture repair kit drew a blank: no one had thought to bring one, though I had a pump. Without ceremony, Jud ransacked the saddlebag Sunbeam's mum had so lovingly packed. Out he flung the sandwiches, spare jerseys, oilskin cape, sou'wester and First Aid kit, all in a heap. Eventually he discovered a repair outfit deep in one of the side pouches. But there were no tyre levers, and without these, even Jud could fathom no way to remove the tyre and repair the tube.

There were cries of, 'Leave him! We're wastin' time pissin' about 'ere! He can walk back!'

From a nearby workshop emanated the din of metal bashing. A gross workman in greasy trousers and filthy white singlet was lounging in the doorway, dragging on a butt and contemplating the scene with quiet amusement. Eventually he waddled over to offer his services. He had the ten-pint-a-nighter's belly of a Sumo wrestler.

'Gi' us that 'ere!' he said. He took the wheel from Jud and gripped it between his knees. Grinning reassuringly, he heaved the tyre side-wards, trying to force it tube and all over the wheel rim. He puffed and strained, his fatty face contorting into the craters of the moon and the snake tattoos on his forearms quivering as if to escape their bonds of skin and slide off down a drain. All to no avail, the brand new tyre wouldn't budge.

He paused, made another face, took a deep wheezy breath and plunged again to the task, this time with result. The spokes twanged, the wheel gave way and he fell backwards in a heap onto the road, cursing.

The tyre remained in place, but now on a wheel that looked as if it had lost an argument with a brick wall. Sunbeam began blubbering again. 'Shurrup!' said the man, scrambling to his feet. 'What's busted can alus be fixed.'

Briefly, he studied the wheel as it lay on the road, then, to our amazement, he jumped on it, his two size-twelve boots crashing down at opposite sides of the rim. Again the spokes twanged, as if some mad harpist were tuning up.

'Sithee,' said the man, holding up and spinning the wheel. 'There's nowt wrong wi' that.'

Anyone could see it was utterly wrecked and would never serve its purpose again.

The man returned the wheel to Jud. 'Ah'll tell thee summat,' he confided. 'Tha'll never get that tyre off wi'out some levers.' As he began to walk away, Sunbeam's blubbering grew to a crescendo of desperation and the man turned back. He dug deep in his pocket. 'Here, kid, here's a tanner. Go buy thissen some spice!' Everyone laughed aloud, except the workman, the irony of Rupert, of all people, being in need of 'spice' entirely lost on him.

Jud made a last minute appeal. 'Haven't you got no tyre levers in that workshop, mister?' But the man disappeared through the doorway into the hellish hammering twilight beyond, like some ancient meddling god of catastrophe.

Jud refitted the wheel and attempted to spin it. But it jammed against the brake blocks and had to be removed. He passed it to Sunbeam. 'There's nowt for it. Thou must walk back home.'

We watched as he set off, wheel in one hand, handlebars in the other, wheeling the bike back towards Sheffield. Gross sobs shook his skinny shoulders.

We never reached Elsecar that day or visited Jud's auntie. Something intervened in the shape of a children's playground on a side road just a mile or so out of Chapeltown. We might well have passed by without stopping had something not winked at us between the trees. It was a copper slide reflecting the brilliance of the afternoon sun. And beside it an iron roundabout, a rocker horse and some swings, all contained in a little grassy park bordering a lane.

First we rushed to the water fountain with its chained iron cup and fought to slake our thirsts. Then, with adolescent whoops of delight, we set about the amusements. Fortunately, we had the park to ourselves, the summer heat having driven mothers and toddlers to take shelter indoors. We stood on the gnarled wooden swing seats and tried to outdo each other, pulling and pushing higher and higher, but without ever quite managing to loop the loop. Two or three together, roaring like lions, we sprinted the roundabout up to top speed, then leapt aboard to lie face up on its baking timber platform. The blue sky spun crazily across our vision and when we closed our eyes, the after-image flashed lighthouse-like on our retinas.

Boredom soon set in. The play fights began: trying to drag each other off the swings and roundabout, trip each other up, wrestle on the grass, fill our mouths with water and spit it out over someone else. My pump was requisitioned as a makeshift air pistol to blast hard, green elderberries. Then Kev, our top tearaway, clambered up the slide, unbuttoned his flies and with a Tarzan yodel, peed down it. A curious

15

knot gathered below to watch the liquid sizzle and evaporate on contact with the red-hot metal, leaving behind a faint multi-coloured stain like a squashed rainbow.

All this while, Jud had lain apart on a grassy bank, detached from the general frolicking as befitted his superior station. Now he sauntered over to join us.

'Pee's acid,' he pronounced, indicating the stain. 'Acid attacks copper.'

I already knew this to be a fact, but had long since learned to keep mum on matters of general knowledge. While Jud could get away with it, I'd have been mocked and called 'grammar school snob'.

His chemistry lesson had a calming effect. He went back to ruminate on the grassy bank and, one by one, the rest of us joined him to hold a verbal replay of the drama that had befallen us in Chapeltown. As we speculated guiltily on Sunbeam's fate, it suddenly dawned on us that there might be parental repercussions. Bomber summed up the general feeling: 'It's not our bloody fault he'd no tyre levers!' But, secretly, we all knew it had been wrong to abandon him.

'What's that yonder?' Kev pointed towards a little wooden hut just beyond the bounds of the playground. We sauntered over for a closer look. The hut was quite dilapidated with peeling blue paint and rusting tin advertising signs tacked to the walls giving the impression these held it together: remove them and the whole edifice might crumble into a heap of worm-eaten matchboard. A small window was shaded by a hinged, wooden blind supported on two metal stays, and in the gloomy interior we could see a counter and shelves with jars of boiled sweets, packets of cigarettes and crisps. But what really caught our attention was the girl standing behind the counter. She was about our age, thirteen upwards, but with blonde hair and pretty, delicate features. Her floral-pattern dress swelled out to fill the contours of blossoming breasts.

'Has anyone got any spice coupons?' asked Bomber hopelessly.

'Ne'er mind t'coupons,' said Tekker. 'Has anyone got any dosh?'

We emptied our pockets and came up with the grand sum of ninepence-halfpenny. Sunbeam the Bountiful was no longer in our midst and we suddenly experienced an acute sense of loss. Tekker was given the task of purchasing crisps and a bottle of Tizer and we all trooped behind him into the shop. At our intrusion, the girl gripped the counter, looking apprehensive, and as she bent down to the bottle crate,

Kev wolf-whistled. Straightening up, she glared angrily and snatched Tecker's money.

Outside again, we passed the Tizer from hand to hand, swigging from the bottle. There was a filthy-fingered scramble for the crisps.

From somewhere, Jud discovered a tanner he had held in reserve and, taking the empty, went back into the shop. He spent a long time at the counter trying to chat up the girl. When he emerged it was with a self-satisfied smirk and a fresh bottle of pop from which he took a long swig before offering it round.

Meantime, Kev had been considering ways to collapse the hut. He rocked it back and forth by shoving his backside against it, grunting like an ape and making obscene gestures. Nothing much resulted except the spice jars slid to and fro on the shelves. Giving up, he turned his attention to the shutter. He high-kicked the stays and the shutter collapsed with a bang, plunging the interior into darkness. Everyone except Jud whooped and cheered. There was a loud squeal from within, the door swung open and the girl confronted us, her blue eyes sparking with rage.

'Stop that at once! My father will be here in a few moments and he will deal with you severely. Make no mistake about it, you'll all be laughing on the other side of your faces!'

We were gob-smacked. It wasn't so much the outburst itself, but her cut-glass accent, perfect English with not a trace of our roughneck Sheffieldish. She stood upright with the presence and authority of a Hollywood schoolmarm in a Western facing down buckaroos the worse for drink. It was evident she had no fear of a bunch of gallumping adolescents. Framed in the doorway, she stared us out until one by one, chastened, we dropped our eyes.

Jud grabbed Kev by the scruff and forced him down to his knees.

'Apologise! Say th'art sorry!'

Kev muttered an unconvincing 'Sor—ry!'

'Again. Properly this time.'

Kev obeyed and Jud frogmarched him to prop the shutter back up.

'He meant no harm, miss. He's just an idiot.' Without another word, the girl stepped back inside her little wooden shack and slammed the door shut.

But 'miss'? That was what got to us. Since when did anyone in our mob address a girl as 'miss'?

Time had slipped past unnoticed. By common consent, it was too late to visit Jud's auntie in Elsecar. Instead, our thoughts turned to the journey home.

As we bobbed and lurched up the hill on the road back towards Sheffield, Jud remarked loudly to all and sundry, 'I reckon that bird fancied me, thou knows.'

Sweating, with sticky dust-grimed mouths, we arrived back on the estate. At once we observed something was wrong. Too many bare-armed mothers were in conversation over the garden gate and, seeing us, each moved swiftly to lay hands on her own. We were for coppit. 'Where've you bin? – Racin' off wi'out tellin' us – Worried sick – Just you wait till Ah tell y'r Dad – Whose idea were it ter leave that Rupert on 'is own? –'

Jud's mother was not amongst this vengeful pack and, seeing the way the wind was blowing, he slunk off muttering, 'Ah've to go for mi tea.'

Evidently, Sunbeam, tired and tearful, had preceded us, after pushing his bike the three long miles home from Chapeltown. He had spilled the beans to his mother, who in turn alerted all the other mothers. It was unlikely they'd much real sympathy for the pampered Sunbeam or his mum with her sparkly earrings and superior airs and graces, but, as was customary on such occasions, they had to put on a communal show of solidarity and disapproval.

Fortunately for me, my own mother was out visiting and the furore had died down before I had to face retribution. It turned out to be nothing more than a mild quizzing over what exactly had led to Sunbeam being abandoned, with an added warning not to allow myself to be influenced by "that gang of boys" and "to remember I was now at grammar school, a Catholic grammar school, and ought to show a good example to the rest."

It only took 'that little snitch Sunbeam' three days to bribe his way back into our social circle and the whole episode soon faded from everyone's memory except mine. That was the end of the so-called Elsecar Cycling Club – except it wasn't, not for me at any rate. Oh no, the events of that day took on a powerful emblematic significance in my mind. All within a few hours I had experienced undreamed-of comedy, drama and glorious anarchy. Under my own steam I had travelled to and from a foreign land bathed in sunny splendour. And how had it happened? What had brought it about? The bicycle. The bicycle that had formerly been my beast of burden and errand had revealed itself as a magic carpet to other worlds of adventure that lay out there waiting to be discovered.

It was to be a life-changing event, sowing the seed for cycling to have me henceforth in its thrall.

My Dad and his bike

1937, aged three with my mother and brother John on holiday

FURIOUS RIDING: JEAN ROBIC

The so-called Fabulous Fifties were a very special time in cycling history. The era marked the last gasp of the mythic hero – Bobet, Coppi, Bartali, Gaul, Koblet, Kubler, Anquetil, Van Steenbergen, Geminiani, Hassenforder and, latterly, Tom Simpson. Not just superb athletes and great champions (as if that were not enough), many were also portrayed in the media as outstanding personalities, 'characters'. In a sport where fact so often mingled with fantasy, some would not have looked out of place amongst the eccentrics of Balzac or Dickens, or the cast list of a *Grand Guignol* opera.

However, setting the media aside, what really distinguishes these men from subsequent cycling stars, largely sprung from the homogeneous postwar European middle-class with its social services safety net, is an upbringing where the struggle for survival was predominant. During their formative years, between 1914 and 1945, Europe was the melting pot of two world wars. Hardship, poverty and actual physical danger went with the territory and in turn promoted an extraordinary degree of self-reliance, boldness, resilience and individuality. It was a breeding ground for quirkiness. Step forward, then, Jean Robic, winner of the 1947 Tour de France, the quirkiest, tiniest, toughest, ugliest, unluckiest of them all.

At 5 feet 3 inches tall and weighing only 9 stones 4 pounds, 'The Mouse of Radenac' was no giant. But what he lacked in physique, he more than made up for in personality. He feared nothing and no one. His remarkable strength of will, determination and bravery (some said foolhardiness) singled him out from an early age.

He was born in 1921 in the small town of Vouziers in the Ardennes, the fourth of five children. The roads in eastern France had been left devastated by the bombardments of the First World War and Jean's father, demobilised in 1919, worked first as carpenter and then foreman on the task of reconstruction. But soon he was yearning for his homeland of Brittany, and when he returned there to the commune of Radenac, he took the family with him. He was proudly independent and hardworking. Not content with being a carpenter, he opened a small cycle shop as a sideline, without realising that this was to provide the springboard for his son's lifelong fascination with the sport. The father, himself a racing cyclist before the war, encouraged Jean. Each morning as a small child, and especially during the Tour de France, he would eagerly read the newspaper for the cycling results before going to school, where he was top of his class, though eventually leaving without a diploma. Not scared of getting his hands dirty, keen to become financially independent, it wasn't long before he found himself a variety of spare-time jobs and was earning his crust.

But the young entrepreneur was not popular with all his acquaintances. In fact some detested him. He could be loud, disputatious and boastful. He had a genius for provoking quarrels and 'shit-stirrer' was a rebuke sometimes flung his way, evidence of a disturbing personality trait. Modern-day psychoanalysis might well have attributed this 'challenging behaviour' to the bout of meningitis he suffered as a young child. There were then no drugs to treat this killer disease and he was lucky to recover, though it probably left its mark thereafter on his emotional life. Amongst the many soubriquets that pursued him through his cycling career, 'biquet' (little mountain goat) and 'cabochard' (roughly translated as 'pig-headed') give some clue to his stubborn wilfulness, supposedly a characteristic of the Breton race. Not surprisingly, he could infuriate his peers. Was he 'bovvered', in the words of TV comedian Catherine Tate's surly teenager? Not in the least. Criticism drove him to even more unrepentant and outrageous behaviour. Typically, he would assert out loud in public, 'It's true, I'm a bad character. But so what?'

This 'so what' bull-in-a-china-shop approach to life brought him many enemies. At the same time, it endeared him to the French public. In newspapers, magazines and on radio, he came across as someone who spoke his mind freely and honestly. His words seemed to come direct from the heart and people listened. He was an exciting sport of nature always likely to overturn the established order, deferring to no one however big their reputation. On the bike, he was predictably unpredictable, capable of launching a surprise attack at the least propitious moment and often from the front of the peloton. In that respect, his aggression is reminiscent of the late Marco Pantani, whose unpredictability likewise evoked blind loyalty from his *tifosi*. At the *Parc des Princes*, following his amazing 1947 Tour de France victory, in which, as a mere regional rider without strong team support, he had defeated all the powerful national squads, a reporter asked, 'Aren't you afraid of making enemies?' Robic beat his chest and roared, 'I haven't enough enemies. Give me some more!' The immense 35,000 crowd of spectators cheered the roof off the stadium.

They loved this country boy with his bonk-defying 'magic home-brew' (two large feeding bottles three parts barley water and one part Calvados brandy). In years to come they would contrast him favourably with the more scientific and meticulously prepared Coppi and Bobet. And even further into the future, booing the 'accountant on wheels', Anquetil, for his unpatriotic scheming, it was perhaps the unsophisticated Robic they were measuring him against. One was all calculation, the other all passion.

How did he begin? In 1939, aged 18, like so many other Bretons before him, he set out for Paris to seek his fortune. Arriving at the Gare de Montparnasse, the country boy immediately got himself lost, strayed onto the Metro and did several complete tours of the system and back to his point of departure, where all along an aunt had been waiting to collect him. He had brought along his bike and this allowed him to work for a wholesale coffee merchant on the Rue d'Anjou delivering packages to retail outlets across the city. (Soon, with the outbreak of war, coffee would be in short supply.) Meantime, each Sunday, he participated in a cycle race, usually in the Vallée de Chevreuse, where on the hills *le petit grimpeur* soon made his presence felt. Before long he was rubbing shoulders with the professionals: Speicher, Leduc, Le Greves, Tassin, Louviot...

But this promising start to his career was soon cut short by events. These were desperate times. In May 1940, the German panzers launched their blitzkrieg invasion, by-passing the French defences on the Maginot Line and then forking to head in one direction for the Channel ports and in the other for Paris. The population had not forgotten the Prussian siege of 1871, when the city had been starved into submission, and in large number began fleeing to the relative safety of the countryside. On 12 June Robic, accompanied by an aunt, both on bicycles, joined one of these southward bound refugee columns. A pedalling beast of burden, he carried on his back two large suitcases. His racing machine had no support for saddlebag or panniers. He could have borrowed or hired a more suitable bicycle, but that would have meant abandoning his precious racer to the plundering whim of invaders and putting his ambitions on hold – war or no war, there was no way this promising young star would bow to such a gospel of despair. The savage brutality of war confronted the bicyclists at Chartres, where they had to dive into the ditch as a Luftwaffe pilot strafed their column. Further down the road, the threat was underlined as they came across the pallid corpses of men, women and children, victims of Hitler's strategy of 'total war'. By the time they reached Le Mans, Jean's back was breaking under the strain and he was forced to purchase a small baggage trailer to attach behind his bike. Thus, cycling from dawn to dusk, they trundled to Radenac, a journey of 450 kilometres in four days. The next afternoon, under a downpour, the villagers witnessed the passage of a single German motorcycle dispatch rider. For them, this lone warrior symbolised the total occupation of France and overwhelming triumph of the Wehrmacht. Their tears mingled with the rain.

But, at least, France's capitulation led to a swift and welcome degree of normalisation. In January 1941 Jean was able to return to his old job in Paris and resume his cycling career. He finished third in Paris–Rouen and eighth in Paris–Alençon. Then, just as he was set to turn professional, the authorities came knocking on his door. He had been drafted into a labour force and set to dig trenches around an airfield under the watchful eye of German sentries. He strove to retain his form by cycling each day the 70 kilometres out and back to the work site at Poissy. However, he soon came to the conclusion that a mere 400 kilometres a week was insufficient for a man of his high ambition. He needed to be shut of this exhausting pick and shovel drudgery and get down to some really serious training, so he bribed an inspector with several pounds of Brittany butter to turn a blind eye to his absence.

All well and good until his Sunday cycle race victories drew him to the attention of the French police. Checking out his presence, or rather lack of it, at the Poissy site, and discovering he had become a ghost worker, they were none too pleased. They came looking for him again, and he was obliged to keep changing addresses, a virtual draft dodger on the run. At the same time, in the course of long training rides around Paris, he was picking up valuable information of a military nature and passing it on to the Resistance, thus, if captured, putting himself in line for severe punishment, even deportation to a slave labour camp in Germany. Nonetheless, he continued racing each Sunday – a courageous act, considering the danger of denunciation he exposed himself to by appearing before the crowds of spectators that formed around these popular events. It seems nothing short of miraculous that he never once had his collar felt by an officiating gendarme.

Perhaps his attitude was not so much courageous as naive. The story is told of him, late in the war, returning from a ride in the country and finding dumped at the roadside a German officer's uniform – a deserter, maybe, or token warning that the Resistance was active. With no other means to transport this 'booty', he put it on – just imagine, a racing cyclist pedalling along in a Wehrmacht cap and jacket and carrying a pair of knee-length leather boots knotted into the spare tubular tyre around his shoulders! Thus 'disguised', he entered Paris, where a friend called him to a halt. 'Are you mad, Jean? If they catch you, they're going to shoot you on the spot.'

Robic shrugged. 'First they've got to catch me. And if they do, I'll say I found a body at the roadside and thought it only right to return the uniform to its proper owners.'

More by luck, then, than judgment, he evaded capture and continued racing throughout the war years, albeit in a limited capacity. But in April 1944, during the course of Paris–Roubaix, something occurred that was to become a treacherous hallmark of his career. He crashed and severely fractured his skull, necessitating a month in hospital. During his 21 years of racing (1940–61), Jean was to break many other bones – wrist, hand, breastbone, shoulder, collarbone, ribs, vertebrae and the renowned craggy nose – some twice over. In the 1946 Paris–Roubaix, he again fractured his skull and thereafter took to wearing that enormous leather helmet. In a comical scene that could have come from *The Three Stooges*, he ordered team-mate André Mahé to put it to the test. Mahé obeyed and with the helmet still on Robic's head fetched him a thwack with a hammer. 'Hmm! Excellent!' Robic remarked. 'I felt absolutely nothing.' A trickle of blood ran down his forehead and onto his cheek.

At a time when 99 per-cent of riders had no more protection for their heads than a light cotton cap, the bobbing trademark helmet singled him out in the peloton. The former nickname of 'glass head' now became *tete de cuir* (leather-head), an apt title in more senses than the obvious. His propensity for crashing out of races seems to have been all at one with his reputation for wilfulness and disregard for danger that marked his time in occupied Paris. There is something inescapably droll about Robic and his accidents. In one of his most famous cartoons, René Pellarin (Pellos) encapsulates those twin traits of his character – nutcase and indomitable brave-heart – that so endeared him to the French public. Awry, wild-eyed, shell-shocked, covered from head to toe in sticking plasters and bandages, the tiny, leather-helmeted Jean can be seen bouncing his bike from pothole to pothole as the towering Alpine peaks, anthropomorphised into malicious giant gods, bend their sneering heads to mock his progress. Each wayside 'milestone' marks another year and another crash. A personified stretcher dances on its hind legs with anticipatory glee. An ambulance, with its rear doors flung open, awaits the next inevitable disaster in a career drawing to its close.

Given his vulnerability to accident, it comes as something of a shock to discover that his first major triumphs happened in cyclo-cross, a branch of cycling that by its very nature seems to challenge the lords of mischance. In 1941, aged only 19, he took fourth place in the Criterium International. Though he was new to the sport which, strangely, had yet to find favour in Brittany, he possessed the ideal character and build for success. The races were disputed both on foot and on the bike. The challenging terrain often encompassed woodland with paths that twisted and turned, and steep climbs and descents on treacherous surfaces. The brusque and violent efforts demanded were perfectly suited to Robic's aggressive character and, being light on his feet and with a low centre of gravity to aid balance, he held an immediate advantage over bulkier, taller competitors. Moreover, as the field quickly broke up, he competed for much of the race alone, thus avoiding the multifarious risks that were part and parcel of mixing it in the big pelotons. At least, if he fell here, the ground was soft and more forgiving.

On Sunday 18 March 1945, whilst remnants of the defeated Germany army were still holed up in the ports of Lorient and Saint Nazaire, the cyclo-cross championship of France took place in the Forest of Fontainebleau. The pre-race favourite was Robert Oubron, later to become a radio commentator and celebrated sporting journalist with *L'Equipe*. But it was Robic who triumphed despite suffering a puncture. Cradling his bouquet, he announced to the crowd, 'Today has brought me joy twice over – for the athlete and for the patriot. Let's be clear what donning this tricolour jersey means.' For Robic it meant recognition for himself as a rising cycling star and a symbol of the rebirth of his beloved France, liberated at last from the Nazi yoke.

Jean's interest in cyclo-cross remained strong until 1950, when he won the first-ever World Championship title on a course through the Bois de Vincennes. Thereafter, having touched the zenith of the sport, he reverted to the road.

But success off-road had convinced him, that of all the classics, Paris–Roubaix was the one he was born to win. As a cyclo-cross star, he thought he had honed to perfection the technical skills required to stay upright over the slippery cobbles of the infamous Hell of the North. Unfortunately, fate determined otherwise. He was well positioned in the lead group in 1944 when he crashed out. The slimy, mud-basted *pavé* with its concealed potholes was again his undoing in 1946 and once more he fractured his skull in the fall. Try as he might in this great classic, ninth place in 1956 was the best he could ever manage.

The Tour de France had been on hold since 1939. Organiser, Jacques Goddet, had promoted other wartime races, but the Tour was something special, an icon of French culture and not to be contaminated by association with the Nazi regime. He therefore doggedly resisted pressure from the German authorities, keen to propagandise the impression of normality in the occupied lands and affirm unity with Vichy France. The war at an end, the French government also sought normalisation and was convinced that resuming the Tour would boost morale. But there were problems. In those parts of France where battles had raged, the infrastructure was still in need of repair. Food was also in short supply and riders could not be expected to race for day after day over long distances simply on fresh air and mineral water. So permission was sought and granted for the supply of extra rations.

But when at long last the Tour resumed in 1947, anti-fascist feelings in France still ran high against former Axis nations. German riders would be excluded for ten years. The 'Italian' team was made up exclusively of Franco-Italians. But no feelings ran so high as Robic's. He had been outraged to be told he had been passed over by the selectors of the French national team. The previous year he had finished third in Monaco–Paris, ostensibly a trailer for the forthcoming Tour. It had been won on general classification over five stages by Apo Lazarides, a protégé of veteran René Vietto, pre-war star and current French team leader. But it was Jean, not René, who had caught the public eye. He had climbed and sprinted with the very best and it took the spoiling action of a 'combo' of the very best finally to thwart him. Despite the two men's intense rivalry, Robic felt sure he had had Vietto's promise of a place at the top table for 1947. On being informed of his omission, he felt betrayed and cheated. In his eyes this was another of Vietto's fixes, like the result of Monaco–Paris. Instead of flaunting on his shoulders the tricolour jersey of France, he had to make do with a place in the West France regional team representing Brittany and Normandy. He was a proud man and here was an affront to his self-esteem that he was not to forget or forgive in a hurry. He swore vengeance. With hindsight, we can recognise this early schism with the French cycling establishment as the fault line that ran through and jeopardised his entire career.

If Vietto dreamed he had thus marginalised the challenge from this troublesome Breton, he was to be rudely awakened. Finishing with the leaders at Brussels and Luxembourg, it was Robic who took the chequered flag at Strasbourg, imposing himself over the favourite, the Swiss Ferdi Kubler. But here it might well have ended in disaster. The young lady chosen to hand out the winner's bouquet, in her enthusiasm, pounced on Jean almost as he crossed the line. She knocked him flying off his bike. He was badly shaken, but for once nothing was broken. Unusually courteous in the circumstances, he picked himself up off the road and, as she planted a kiss on his cheek, remarked, 'You're very pretty, mademoiselle, but you could well have done me a deal of damage!'

Three days later, in the mountains between Lyon and Grenoble, it was Robic who did the damage, taking his second stage in magisterial fashion. He led the way over every col. And even better for the little Breton, his rival Vietto lost the yellow jersey he had worn since stage two to the 'Italian' Aldo Ronconi. It was to be a brief joy, however. On the road to Digne, Jean was first over the Izoard and the Vars, but a puncture cost him the stage. Vietto won and snatched back the lead.

By the Pyrenees, Robic had a deficit of 25 minutes, a seemingly impossible handicap for him to overcome. But the man himself begged to differ and said as much to the press. When his comments became public, the French team were scornful. 'The little dwarf has a big gob,' they chuckled, 'but Vietto will have him for breakfast.' Before them all lay the toughest stage of the Tour: Luchon to Pau. They fully expected Robic's challenge to crumble in the high mountains. Instead, irritated by their insults, he hurled himself into the attack from the start and was soon out on his own. He was determined to cover himself in glory or die in the attempt. Solo, he crossed each of the great cols – Peyresourde, Aspin, Tourmalet, Soulor, Aubisque – adding their time bonuses to his lead of 11 minutes at the finishing line in Pau. It was a devastating response to his critics.

Still Vietto clung to his yellow jersey. He was to lose it between Vannes and Saint-Brieuc in a 139-kilometre time trial, which to this day remains the longest in Tour history. The distance was more than Vietto's ageing legs could cope with and he suffered an extraordinary *defaillance*. Moreover, so the story goes, Robic had contrived to have food parcels delivered from the farming heartland of Brittany (remember the butter bribe?) and so was better nourished than the city boys. This was Robic's homeland and, spurred on by his supporters who lined the route, he gave it all he had. Though beaten into second place by the Belgian Impanis, he nevertheless rose to third on general classification behind the two 'Italians' Pierre Brambilla and Ronconi. Now only 2–56 separated him from the coveted *maillot jaune*.

Tour de France 1947, Robic on the Col de Peyresourde

The next day, Saint-Brieuc to Caen, Robic attacked repeatedly, but failed to dislodge Brambilla from his wheel. And so to the final stage, a whopping 268 kilometres to Paris, that seemed almost certain to become a procession culminating in a bunch sprint for the line at the *Parc des Princes*. Brambilla looked as if he had it in the bag. Jean's own *directeur sportif* insinuated as much when he came to awaken him at 6.00 a.m. saying, 'Third place in the Tour de France, for you that's not at all bad.' He was trying to comfort Jean at a time when he assumed he would be biting the bullet of despair. The thanks he got for his words of consolation came in the form of a pair of shoes flung at his head together with a few choice oaths. Jean Robic beaten? Never! Never would he acknowledge defeat!

At Rouen, 160 kilometres from the finish, just after the feeding station, Robic stormed off alone up the côte de Bonsecours. Unaware that a small break, including the eventual stage winner, Briek Schotte, was already up the road, he mistakenly thought he had won the prime prize for being the race leader over the summit. *'Vas-y, Biquet!'* cried his partisan supporters from the roadside. With no other game plan, he simply put his head down and went. Brambilla, caught for a moment off guard, countered and got back to him. The indefatigable Robic then attacked again. Once more Brambilla fought back. Now the pair were joined by Edouard Fachleitner of the French national team and he in turn took off alone. This time only the Breton proved capable of closing the gap. Fachleitener, who was in fourth place overall behind Brambilla, had ambitions to win the Tour for himself, but now he perceived Robic was too strong, and when the Breton offered him a payment of 100,000 francs for his services, he accepted. The lead grew as the two Frenchmen worked together to distance themselves from the exhausted Italian. But the picture was complicated when another Tricolour, Lucien Teisseire, a sworn enemy of Robic, dropped back from the break and joined the two escapees. Whilst Robic might pay for Fachleitner's services, bribing Teisseire to work for him was totally out of the question. Teisseire's purpose was to obstruct.

The drama continued right to the line. At Marly on the outskirts of Paris, Robic crashed on the cobblestones after tangling bikes with Teisseire. But nothing could stop him. Later he said, 'It was as if a raging wind carried me on its wings.'

Al Stiller, an American trackman from Chicago, had been racing that day on the pink cement track of the *Parc des Princes*. In his memoir, he describes the reception that awaited Robic and his two companions. The stadium capacity was 30,000, but 35,000 spectators had crushed inside and thousands more were clamouring for admission at the gates. There was uproar when news came through via the radio commentary that Jean was in the lead. A Frenchman was about to win the postwar Tour de France! Somehow it was symbolic of the restoration of French pride and honour. Robic did not dispute the sprint. He sat up and freewheeled, raising his arms and milking his triumph for all it was worth. Thus he won the 1947 Tour, with a lead of 3–58 over Fachleitner and 10–07 over Brambilla, and without once wearing the yellow jersey apart from the one that President Gaston Monnerville presented him with that day. His revenge over the French National team was all the sweeter because he was convinced his fall at Marly had been no accident, but contrived by Teisseire as a desperate measure to prevent him, the 'regional', from winning.

He had achieved the seeming impossible and a touch of immortality by becoming the only rider in race history to win the Tour on the last day when that stage had not been a time trial. Poor 'Italian' Brambilla! He had snatched defeat from the jaws of victory. It was scant consolation to him that he had won the King of the Mountains trophy. In a gesture of despair akin to Van Gogh cutting off his own ear lobe, he buried his bicycle at the bottom of his garden.

At the church in Radenac, where as a boy Jean had sung in the choir, the bells rang out to alert the village to the good news: 'Our Jean has won the Tour de France!'

Now, it seemed, Robic had the world of cycling at his feet. But, as it turned out, this was to be the apotheosis of his career. His boast 'Give me more enemies' was to prove his undoing. He was far too abrasive ever to become popular with the French cycling establishment and now, though they could no longer deny him his place in the national team, they found other ways to put the truculent Breton in his place. The Tricolours betrayed him in 1948, when, despite being well positioned himself, he was ordered to wait behind for Louison Bobet. For the 1949 Tour, he was unjustifiably relegated to the Ouest-Nord regional team and told he must prove himself all over again. That year, despite breaking his saddle on the Izoard, he won the crucial stage to Luchon and finished fourth overall in Paris, behind the Italian Bartali. Bobet, the rider preferred over him, had abandoned.

Jean's banishment from the national squad lasted until 1952. Riding as a 'regional', he had been 12th in 1950 and 27th in 1951, decent performances but nothing to suggest he could ever recapture his former glory. So what lay behind his 1952 reselection? The fact was that the French were desperate to break the cycle of foreign domination – the Italians Bartali and Coppi in 1948 and 1949, and the Swiss Kubler and Koblet in 1950 and 1951. In 1952, Bobet was in poor health and elected not to take part. Leading up to the Tour, Coppi was back at his best and odds-on favourite to win. But Robic also had raced consistently well in the early-season classics. In the absence of Bobet, he was chosen as the specialist climber best able to counter the Italian threat posed in the mountains. He possessed all the qualities to fulfil that role with the added bonus of self-belief. 'Coppi?' he said.

'Leave him to me and I will sort him out.' What sounded like an empty boast was, in fact, a view shared by none other than the Italian team manager, Alfredo Binda, a star of the 1920s, who later remarked that Robic was the only rider that Bartali and Coppi really feared in the mountains.

This time *Cabochard* drove a hard bargain. He condescended to rejoin the French team only on the clear understanding that he would share 'protected rider' status with Geminiani, Lazarides, Lauredi and Dotto. It was to be a team ostensibly with five potential leaders, a seeming recipe for rivalry and division. Moreover, he demanded that his closest friend and supporter, Robert Bonnaventure, be also included in the team. Though not himself taking part, Bobet remained the putative leader-in-waiting, power broker and ghost in the machine. When the terms of the deal came to his attention, he choked over his *potage* and it took all of Bidot's diplomatic skill to talk him round.

Robic remained in good form when the Tour departed from Brest. Coppi quickly showed that he was master, yet Jean stuck to the task, remarking in typical forthright fashion that he intended to 'do for' the *Campionissimo*. The question was, apart from his personal domestique Bonnaventure, how many others of the twelve man team could he rely upon? A partial answer came on Alpe d'Huez, included for the first time in the race itinerary. At the foot of this long, daunting ascent, Robic attacked and was soon out in front alone. There was no sign of Coppi – at least not until three kilometres up the climb, when glancing back, to his astonishment, he saw his 'team-mate' Raphael Geminiani with the Italian in tow. Much thanks, Gem! The plucky Breton relaunched his attack, but this time Coppi countered in person and took flight to a stage victory that brought with it the yellow jersey. Jean had confirmed his credentials as a great climber, crossing the finishing line at the summit of Alpe d'Huez in second place at only 1–20 adrift of the Master, with Ockers, Bartali and Geminiani all trailing far behind in his wake.

The next day, the crucifying Sestrieres stage was the scene for yet another show of Coppi's dominance as he passed first over every col – Croix de Fer, Télégraphe, Galibier, Mont Genèvre. Throughout, Robic was hot in pursuit, until, descending from Mont Genèvre, he ran into a patch of gravel and suffered a slow puncture. Where was the French support vehicle at this crucial moment in the race? Marcel Bidot had chosen to follow Nello Lauredi, who was ten minutes down, rather than Jean who was battling it out up front with Coppi. To Bidot, this tactic made good sense because at the start of the stage, Lauredi was fourth overall to Robic's tenth and so, based on 'form', Lauredi merited the crown of team leader. But it made absolutely no sense to poor Jean, limping to the finish and losing over 11 minutes to Coppi. He had been obliged to stop five times en route to inflate the offending tyre, despite which he still finished nine minutes in advance of 'teacher's pet' Lauredi. Undoubtedly, it was this misfortune that cost him second place on the podium in Paris.

Biquet was apoplectic. He lost no time in telling anyone and everyone prepared to listen that this had been another fix and that Bidot had deliberately left him to fend for himself. The truth was more prosaic. It turned out that the French support vehicle had simply run out of petrol and become stranded. It was not so much conspiracy as cock up. But try explaining that to Old Leather-head.

To Biquet's credit, he never gave up. Tenacity was second nature to him – that and aggression. Someone once described him as 'a wound-up spring in cycling shorts'. Next day he was on the attack again, first over the second category Col de Tende and seventh in Monaco, clawing back 11 seconds from Coppi. On stage 14, Aix en Provence to Avignon, still burning with rage at the perceived injustice done to him, he distanced everyone on the slopes of Mont Ventoux and finished in first place. Coppi was in a small select group at 1–37 behind the testosterone-fuelled Breton, with commentators drawing the conclusion that he had treated himself to a 'rest day'. Robic had done what he could in the circumstances, performing with enormous élan and courage, but nothing short of accident was going to stop *Il Campionissimo* from winning his second Tour, literally by several miles. Robic had to be satisfied with fifth place, his second best result since 1947. In the eyes of the French public, he was a great patriotic hero, whereas Bidot, 'the villain' of the piece, was so maligned for his perceived incompetence that he needed protection crossing the Pyrenees.

At the Parc des Princes Biquet was applauded as if he, and not Coppi, was the victor. 'It's only to be expected,' said a magnanimous *campionissimo,* smiling wrily. 'He was the only rider who made me sweat.'

There was no way now, after the 'misunderstandings' of 1952, that Cabochard and the French team would ever be reconciled. The *grand seigneur* Bobet was back in charge in1953 and in sizzling form, about to embark on his hat trick of victories and all the more resolute in his determination to be protected by a team that he could count on one hundred per cent. For the second and final time, Robic was banished to L'Equipe de L'Ouest, becoming a regional rider again alongside François Mahé and Jean Mallejac.

Bobet may have finished with him, but he was not finished with Bobet, not by a long chalk. By winning the Cauerets–Luchon stage, he seemed to cock a snook at his Breton rival. It was not so much that he won this first Pyrenean battle, but the manner in which he did it. In a style reminiscent of *Il Campionissimo,* unleashing attack upon attack, first to the summit of every col – Tourmalet, Aspin, Peyresourde – and despite two falls en route, he stamped his dominance on the field. Koblet, so called 'pedaller of charm' and race favourite, abandoned. Bobet was humiliated, losing 9–12 to the rider he had spurned, whilst Jean, for the first time since 1947, donned the Golden Fleece.

Was this a sign, commentators wondered, that his luck was about to change for the better? In a word, *non.* Bobet, only fourth on general classification, counter-attacked on the road to Albi. Robic gathered his faithful Bretons together and set about closing the gap. But on a downhill, with hands off to take a drink, his wheel hit a pothole and he crashed. It was a bad one. Covered in blood, barely conscious, he set off in pursuit. 'I pedalled like an automaton,' he later told journalists. 'I had no idea where I was or where I was going. I could barely see. I rode the bike like I was playing an accordion, my speed up and down, the pace sometimes so slow I almost fell off, sometimes so fast I outdistanced my companions.' For little Biquet, so badly injured, it was 180 kilometres of Calvary. Somehow he struggled on to the finish, 45 minutes down on the Bobet group. His yellow jersey passed to team-mate Mallejac, who had been given the task of marking Louison.

Robic had cracked five vertebrae. For the first time in all his Tour outings, he was forced to abandon and cede the field to Bobet. Journalists dubbed him, 'misfortune's favourite son'. And it didn't stop there. This was only the start of a black period in his career. In 1954, whilst lying in fourth position on general classification, he crashed into a cameraman and broke his collarbone. In 1955 he crashed time and again in the rain and ended up packing it in between Monaco and Marseille alongside many other riders. Was it time for him to give up altogether? 'Oh, no! I'm only 34. I'm still young. And with Bobet winning every Tour whilst I'm left lying in a hospital bed – it really screws me up!' In 1956, he was put out of the Tour a month before it began, due to injuries sustained on the bike when in collision with a car. In 1957, the organiser, Goddet, wrote him a letter in which he voiced what many others no doubt thought: 'You're too old for the Tour, Jean. I forbid you to start.' I imagine it wasn't Robic's age that was troubling him so much as his appalling accident record. He had become a liability to other riders as well as himself. A fatality – heaven forbid – was not the sort of publicity Goddet craved for France's showcase cycling event and he would carry the can.

Whatever people thought of Jean, they could not help but admire his sheer guts and determination. He never stopped pestering Goddet to be readmitted to the ranks of *La Grande Boucle*, and in 1959, the year that I started in the Tour, the tough-guy organiser relented, a moment of weakness he would regret. Only three stages in and the seeming inevitable happened: Robic crashed. It occurred on the cobbled road to Roubaix, a place that always seemed to bode ill for the little Breton. In the fall, he fractured his wrist. His team manager pleaded with him to call it a day, but Cabochard dug in his heels. He knew this Tour was to be his swansong and nothing could persuade him to abandon. So, with his wrist strapped up, he raced on – through the Pyrenees and Alps, the heat and rain, every jolt a spasm of pain stabbing up his arm and into his shoulder. It was a sort of pilgrimage, a last offering of courage and suffering to his public. It came to an end with only two stages left, when, utterly exhausted, he finished outside the time limit and was eliminated. He was almost there, only two stages left, a time trial and the traditional procession to Paris. He begged to be allowed to continue. But no! Goddet turned his back, and as for the rest of them – well, hadn't he made too many enemies? Even his wife's plea that she had already bought a new dress for the *Parc des Princes* cut no ice with Goddet.

Jean was now 38. At that age, lesser men might have quit in despair, but not Cabochard. He carried on racing for two more years, risking his own neck and others in the hurtling frenetic pelotons until he was 40. A racing cyclist in spirit and name since childhood, he knew nothing else. Sadly, misfortune dogged his long career. He was a star whose brilliance had been wasted in the war years and after by his wrangling with the power brokers of French cycling. At the same time, it must be admitted he was also his own worst enemy, courting controversy with every poisonous tit-bit that fell from his lips. Of

Geminiani's pretensions to stardom, he said, 'Don't make me laugh!' Of Bobet's 'poncy' concern with appearance: 'Louisette Bonbon – for a Breton he's all show!' And again, 'I've got two Bobets in each leg.' Even twenty years after his retirement, journalists would seek him out for the telling comment. In 1980 he mocked former Tour winner and King of the Mountains, Lucien Van Impe: *'Grimpeur?* I could take his bike, fasten a trailer behind with my mother-in-law sitting in it and climb Tourmalet smoking my pipe.' Neither modesty nor tact was his prime virtue. After his 190-kilometre solo breakaway to victory at Pau he had christened himself 'Prince of the Pyrenees'. He claimed to be so gifted at school that his teacher took him on as his deputy. His visiting card similarly gilded the lily. Beside his *palmarés* appeared two mythic bravery awards: *'Chevalier de l'Ordre Nichan Iftikar'* and 'Distinguished Service Cross of General Patton', neither of which has proved verifiable. He had a droll sense of humour, and the charitable view is that his outrageous remarks were part and parcel of a lifelong, tongue-in-cheek campaign of self-promotion – a commercial instinct that is not the same thing as boasting.

For me, there is a mystery at the heart of Robic. How did he reconcile his bad-boy image with being a devout Roman Catholic? How often on his knees in the confessional box did he have to beg God's forgiveness for his sins of vanity, braggadocio, profanity and wilful slander, only to emerge shriven and ready to commit the same sins all over again? In his later life he wore a penitential hair shirt next to his skin.

His career after cycling followed a bumpy path. From being someone famed for stick-ability, he jumped grasshopperlike from job to job: restaurateur, newspaper delivery agent, removals man, wrestling match referee and even inventor, exhibiting at the Paris *Concours Lepine.* Unlike his more refined and diplomatic contemporaries, Bobet and Anquetil, he was rarely called to the service of the media. He had overdone the bad mouthing and displeased too many in high places, where it counted.

I have always been a great fan of Robic, though the little gremlin never found much favour this side of the Channel with the small band of brother cyclists at my grammar school, who gathered near the bike sheds at lunchtime to ogle the stars in *Miroir Sprint* magazine. Robic's battered-boxer visage inspired much finger stabbing and sniggering (Doh! That daft helmet! The nose! Those big ears!). But being an object of ridicule obscured his real merit. Secretly, I admired the courage of this underdog, glorious in victory and glorious in defeat. When, during my sojourn in France, I finally came to compete with him, it was with the realisation that his star was fast sinking, his best days long gone. Now divorced from his wife, he presented a sad and lonely figure, relic of a bygone age, standing on the *ligne de départ*, craggy, scarred, the gross leather helmet squashed onto the face of a pantomime Mother Twanky, the young riders seemingly giving him wide berth, perhaps the superstitious Italians grasping their testicles in the left hand in the Neapolitan manner to ward off the evil eye of misfortune. Given the choice, no one willingly followed his superlatively accursed wheel. It led to the deepest pothole, the wrong angle to cross the treacherous tramlines, the multi rider pile-up on a straight road with perfect daylight visibility, the Hound from Hell that lay in wait for Robic, and Robic alone, to clasp his calf in its jaws as he passed and bring him to ground. It led to the Aspro ambulance, the dread helicopter, the hospital, perhaps even the morgue. It was therefore fitting that he died not with a whimper but a bang, in a road accident, inexplicably crashing his car into a trailer on 6 October 1980. Perhaps if this curiously pious, scapular-wearing Catholic could have returned to explain himself, he might have shrugged his shoulders and said God had told him to do it. 'This is the moment, Biquet, and there's the gap. So go for it!' And go for it he did.

BEING ROBIC

November 1949, late afternoon. A teenage boy jolts down the steps of his school, cursing under his breath. Everything is so unjust. Outraged, he crosses the quad out of sight of the office, towards the bike sheds, pausing at a cast-iron planter with its withered offering of long-dead chrysanthemums. *Labor Omnia Vincit* – the engraved Latin tag springs out at him, adding insult to injury. So work is the solution to everything? Well, so be it. With deliberate timing and chanting each word like a mantra, he chops the web-stuck stalks down with hefty shoe swings, invoking his hated taskmaster: 'You – old – bastard – Donovan!' Detained twenty minutes, and for why? Forgetting to underline the date, one of Donovan's stupid golden rules, a pencil line, for Christ's sake. So now it's payback and he'll do as the tag tells him, and it's Donovan's desiccated brains he's kicking in, and that brown debris that swirls away on the breeze is all that's left of Donovan's sick, old grey head. A good kicking! Hard labour. Yet still he feels unrequited.

Mocking applause greets his action. He turns his attention towards the bike sheds' mossy corrugated canopy and espies two bowed shapes gesticulating, screwing their index fingers into their foreheads and guffawing at him like loons. Warner and sidekick Conroy! The scumbags should have gone home at the closing bell. So what's kept them back to pleasure at his expense? Then he remembers. Of course, Conroy's new bike! Conroy must have ridden his new bike back into school just to swank it off in front of Warner.

'No guts!' Warner scoffs. 'You let that old Donovan piss all over you.'

'So would you've.'

'Like hell! Those Brothers don't push me around. Here, Mikey, we've something to show you.'

When he reaches the sheds, he sees they have Conroy's bike concealed under their school blazers, as if he's not supposed to know it's there. One of their stupid little tricks, no doubt, and them grinning from ear to ear, the bastards! He swallows hard. They cup their hands and tip back their heads to make a trumpet blast – Ta-ra-ra-rar! – then whip away the coats.

And yes, yes – the revelation almost takes his breath away. It's too much. He runs greedy eyes up and down the bike, exposed in all its naked beauty like some gleaming arty model in *Men Only*. Oh yes, this is pure lust. The sheer brilliance of the thing! That blue and red enamelling, the gleam of the slender Brooks racing saddle, the honky South of France bars with brake levers at just the right cocky angle, the shocking green of the cloth tape wound right up to the stem in the genuine style, the honey-coloured chain and blue-burnished rollers of the four speed Simplex derailleur – the rims, pedals, cranks, everything glittering brand new even in the gloom of the shed. And what about those tyres with their virginal showroom glaze? My God, real Pirellis, real tubulars! The bike must have cost an absolute fortune.

'So, what d'you reckon, mister expert?' Warner demands.

'It's OK.'

'OK!' splutters Conroy. 'OK? Are you blind or what? It's spanking brand new and a damned sight better than your old wreck.' He indicates Michael's decrepit 1930s sports cycle slumped at the end of the rack.

'Conroy passed his exams like a good little boy,' Warner sneers, 'and Daddy said, "Take your pick." So he did.'

That explains everything. The spoiled brat and his rich parents, all it takes to possess such a wonderful machine. But will Conroy ever use it? Really use it? Somehow Michael can't see it, can't see him burning it up with the gang, sprinting for 30 signs, climbing Snake Pass and Mam Tor, coming home exhausted and soaked in sweat after dark. No! It's just for show, just for flaunting in front of his drooling so-called mates, a showcase bike. Michael feels sick with envy. What he would give to possess something like this, but it's a dream and way beyond his parents' means.

'It's a Paris,' says Warner. 'There's the Eiffel Tower to prove it.' He points at a badge on the head tube.

Paris! Even the name thrills – though Warner delivers each cunningly chosen word through the curled lips of contempt.

'Come on, Mikey, we await your true verdict. After all, you're our future. You're tomorrow's great British cycling star. Imagine – *Le Criterium des As*. You're out-sprinting Kubler on your Paris, and then suddenly – Craaack! – that weird bottom bracket snaps off and you crash out.'

There it is absolutely staring him in the face, and yet for all his wrapt adoration he's somehow missed it, the frame's unique feature, that foreshortened seat tube and the bottom bracket that seems to hang only half supported in midair. To hide his confusion, he adopts his mock professorial voice. 'I couldn't possibly comment without subjecting this pedal-cycle to a rigorous trial,' adding, 'give us a go then, Conroy.'

The Paris 'Galibier'

Conroy, puffed up, appears deaf.

'It's the Galibier model,' he blurts. 'What Fausto Coppi rides.'

Warner snorts. 'Coppi, my arse! He rides for Bianchi. Any mutt knows that.'

Silent, Michael defers to the armchair bike-racing connoisseur, who shows off his command of French at break times translating *But et Club* to a small audience of enthusiasts behind this same shed.

'Just think, with Conroy's brains and a rich daddy, this could've been your bike, Mikey.'

'What about you?'

40

'Moi? Je n'en ai pas besoin. I don't have your high aspirations to become the big star.' Warner swaggers with a two-fisted salute to show how tall the big star walks.

Michael persists. 'Let's have a go on it, Conroy.'

'My Dad says no one's to ride it but me.'

'Keeping it in a showcase? Hell, man! It's a bike! It's for riding! Come on, I won't hurt it. Just round the quad. Who's to know?'

'Suppose my Dad –?'

'Who's to tell him?'

'Well, the Brothers might.'

'The Brothers are all up the Big House having tea. Come on, Conroy. Round the quad. Just once. What's the harm?'

Gently, he lifts the bike out of Conroy's reluctant hands, testing its weight. Feather light! He gets astride, wriggles his clumsy school shoe into the toe clip and pushes off, circling the quad, getting the feel for it.

So lively! Round he goes, leaning in to the corners, one crank raised. Round and round. Faster. Faster. Change up. No chattering or grinding from this A1 bike, but the smooth precision of a chain flicking home on a sprocket.

'That's enough,' shouts Conroy, panicking as Michael skims the school walls. 'Give it back! Now!' Warner laughs maniacally and Michael senses the same mad spook enter his own soul. Why not try a sprint, test it to destruction? See if its strength matches its elegance?

He lines the bike up, jumps and sprints down the quad, braking hard to make a wobbly turn beside the office. Then back again, turning and fending Conroy off with a rugby shove. Oh, it's good to hear the little rat squeal.

He's up to full power again when a school fire door crashes open and out steps a black-gowned shape, barring his path. Instinctively, he slaps on the anchors and the bike pirouettes, pitching him onto the tarmac.

Christ! The impact! – his hand's taken the fall's full force. He rolls free of the machine to stare at a pair of polished boots under the hem of a black soutane as pain lashes up to his armpit.

'Get up, you idiot!' Principal Brother Francis, bespectacled face purple-stormy, is standing over him. 'In the name of Holy Mary, what are you up to?' – his voice savage as a chimney peat fire in a Galway gale. 'Isn't the quad out of bounds for such capers? And what's this ridiculous object?' He toes the Paris with disgust. 'A pedal-cycle? Surely not, it looks more like something made in a mad monk's workshop.'

Conroy runs up to retrieve his machine, with Warner sauntering behind.

'Take your hands from your pockets, lad.' The Brother roars so loud it's like a face slap. 'Into my office, all three of you.' Under the quizzical gaze of the twin Sacred Heart and Blessed Virgin statues that adorn his desk, they stand in a shuffling, uncomfortable line as the Brother sits, detaching his rolled belt from the pocket beside his rosary and thumping it down as if that too has given offence.

'Now, Conroy' – his sudden affability is threatening, – 'why have I invited you in here?' Conroy looks blank.

'Well, do you imagine I've been racking my brains over some abstruse problem of Religion or Philosophy and bethought myself to call upon these great scholars Warner and Ryan for help?'

Conroy understands sarcasm. It falls upon his ears often enough. Uncertain, he smiles foolishly until Warner unexpectedly resolves his dilemma.

'Hardly!'

'Hardly? Hardly what?' snaps the Principal.

'You're hardly likely to be asking anything of the likes of us.'

'*Brother*! One: no one asked you to interject, boy, and, two: you know well enough by now to address me by my proper title.' The Principal's eyes narrow as he focuses on the boy's necktie. 'And what on earth is that rag you have around your neck?'

Warner smirks, fingering the enormous, gaudy knot inside the spiked collar of his floral fashion shirt. Barely concealed under his blazer, he is dressed for the dancehall, his overlong hair slicked behind in the duck-arse mode.

'That, Warner, is not school uniform. You dare present yourself before me in such disgraceful attire? Lower Sixth Form you may be, but beware of getting too big for your boots. You will report to me first thing tomorrow morning.

Michael has been listening with half an eye on the rolled strap. In the warmth of the office it is beginning to slowly uncurl like a snake rousing from slumber. Now Warner's got the Brother's goat, there's no telling what might happen next.

'Conroy, I'm surprised you allowed this idiot Ryan anywhere near your pedal-cycle, but knowing him I suppose he tricked you?'

Michael perceives the way it's going, to divest Conroy of blame. Oh, his wealthy parents and their cutlery business and those fat cheques to the School Fund – it all has to be managed with discretion.

'I let him sit astride it, Brother,' Conroy falters, 'just to try it for size.'

'And you took off and went haring around the quadrangle without permission, didn't you, Ryan? You said, "To hell with school rules and the risk of me injuring someone and wrecking someone else's property. To hell with my friend, Conroy! I shall do exactly as I please." Isn't that so?'

Michael thinks it best to agree. But the Brother isn't finished yet. He sees fit to wring a moral from the occasion.

'And where did you obtain this two-wheeled abomination, Conroy?'

Conroy explains at some length how and where the Paris originated, even naming the shop and the price. A pinch of disgust furrows the Brother's forehead. 'What?' Oh, the hair shirt pricks at his skin with the thought of this wasteful profligacy and the object itself, the bicycle, so gaudy, misshapen, useless and trivial! 'Your parents must have more money than sense!' he blurts, biting his lip almost at once.

Silence. A sudden uneasy truth flutters up and around the office and hangs like a butterfly before landing on Warner's darting tongue. To Michael's horror, he spits it back.

'Should he tell them you said so, Brother?'

Now Michael, helpless to intervene, understands. Warner is looking for a fight. He has his shoulders back and that challenging smirk on his face as the Brother Principal reddens and points an angry quivering finger.

'What was that you said? Repeat your words, Warner. You dare to interrogate me? This is the last straw!' He tears off his spectacles, snatches up the belt and comes around the desk, indicating for the boy to raise his hand. 'Your rudeness is some abominable devil crying out to be expelled and tamed. I shall not hesitate to do my duty.'

Exulting in the deliberate provocation, lanky Warner towers above the enraged, grey-haired Principal. With Conroy and Michael as witnesses, he will surely take the six blows on each hand like a martyr and then, later, outside, fists in the air, just as surely swagger like a brave champion of misrule.

Brother Francis bends his shoulder into the strokes. The flayed strap hisses through the air, landing each time with the crack of a pistol shot. Beads of sweat feather his brow and by the end he is breathing hard. Warner has barely blinked. Now it's Michael's turn, three on each hand, the first like a bolt of electricity inducing numbness, the rest merely stinging like a bad nettling. Brother Francis has not heeded his injured hand and now as the blows open up the cut, blood drips onto the wood-block floor. The long-sighted Brother doesn't notice. From his black soutane the vigorous exercise releases a faint perfume of incense and tobacco.

When it comes to Conroy, he says, 'I shall speak to your parents. That will be punishment enough.' Exhausted, the old man flops down behind his desk and waves them from his presence.

Sucking his torn palm, Michael collects his bike from the shed, whilst Conroy inspects the Paris for damage. Miraculously, it has escaped scratch-free. The three boys, bonded now as never before, walk together to the tall, wrought-iron entrance gates.

'That was some beating,' says Conroy admiringly.

I've had worse.' Warner, sardonic, appears untouched. 'I just feel sad for that old perv. How else does he get his kicks but by belting us? I'll bet he's in the cloakroom now, jerking off!'

They all roar, none louder than Conroy, uneasy at his escape. But now Warner is all fired up to make a speech.

'Hey, look at Mikey's hand.' He holds it up in dramatic display, like some latter-day Caesar addressing the Roman mob. Slicing the palm diagonally from thumb to little finger, a livid cut coruscates like raw meat. 'Take inspiration from the blood,' he exclaims, letting the hand fall. 'What d'you say, Mikey? *Il faut apprendre à souffrir, car c'est la seule grande loi du Tour.** Who spoke those words? I'll tell you. It was Jean Robic, little Biquet, through gritted teeth and sweat and pain, climbing the cols to victory. *Quel champion!* You must learn to suffer

---

* You must learn to suffer, for that is the one great law of the Tour.

like Robic if you're ever to become a great *coureur*, Ryan! Forget the bike! Think only of the pain and forget that too! Take inspiration from the suffering! Adios, amigos!'

With a casual wave and his practised two-fisted salute, he who has learned to suffer swaggers off down the leaf-strewn path into the November gloom.

Michael slowly shakes his head. Is this a genuine compliment or just another studied sneer? But Warner is right about Robic. He can see him now in his mind's eye, the darling of the beret-crowned crowds, leather-helmeted, necklace of spare tyre and goggles, bobbing up the great cols in the Tour de France, hands clenched either side of the stem, with the agonised Christ-like face of one who wills himself to victory – *Quel champion!*

'Race you to the top of the hill!'

Conroy is already astride the Paris and six lengths up as the gas lamps on the avenue flutter to life. Michael tears after him. He can feel the dead weight of his machine, the heavy tyres sucking the road, the torpor of the steel cranks and pedals, the old, worn chain grinding fit to snap and the pain of his torn hand as he wrenches at the bars. But all that suppressed electric rage drives him on. He overhauls the Paris and gut-thrashes over the summit, flinging a triumphant arm high in the air. He ignores Conroy's pathetic cry of, 'Hang on!' and takes off down the other side, accelerating.

He's just topped Bonsecours. Left the field trailing. Gone through the pain barrier like Robic. Solo! No one can hold his wheel. And now again he's Robic – Paris–Roubaix, racing through the rainstorm, all clarted in mud but spirit unvanquished – *Quel champion!*

Rattling down over the cobbled, tram-lined roads towards the chequered flag of the steel city and home, he rejoices in a great rush of adrenaline – Michael Ryan, sixteen, schoolboy on his old battered bike, but at that moment, being Robic, envying no one.

THE FRATERNITY OF THE BUCKSHEE WHEELERS

I like to think cyclists can be somewhat akin to rabbits. Two of them meet up in some god-forsaken hole, metaphorically rub noses and within weeks they have multiplied into a club. I hasten to add this is through social intercourse rather than any other rabbity habit you may have in mind. Cyclists are a chummy lot. And there is no better example of this than the story of the Buckshee Wheelers.

1941 saw WW2 reaching a crucial phase. Rommel's army was advancing across the Western Desert with the objective of breaking through to Alexandria, Cairo and beyond to Iraq and India, severing our supply lifeline through the Suez Canal, a catastrophe from which we would be unlikely to recover. The Eighth Army, including the famous 'Desert Rats', Wavell's 30,000, was falling back from Benghazi and Tobruk to form a defensive line close to the tiny railway halt at Al Alamein, and General Montgomery's appointment to command and inspire was still in the future. Rommel and the Nazis seemed invincible and for those of us back home in blitzed Britain, despite cheerful, chins-up propaganda to the contrary, the daily newspaper war maps painted a gloomy picture of defeat and retreat.

So was there ever a less auspicious time or place to start a new cycling club?

The man behind the Buckshee Wheelers was Johnnie Walker, a racing member of the Sheffield Central and Oval CC. Johnnie had volunteered for army service at the outbreak of war in September 1939 and by October had been promoted to sergeant and posted to General Staff Intelligence at HQ Cairo. In common with most servicemen, he left his bike back home in Blighty. But now, finding he had some spare time on his hands, he heard through the grapevine that a certain Charlie Damien, a notable time trialist of that era, had a machine for sale and he took up the offer. During a ride on this bike around Cairo he met a civilian cyclist called Paddy Roebuck, a 60+ veteran in the employ of Marconi Ltd. who had an office in the city. The men quickly formed a club of two, which soon became three as they added Olympic Games sprinter Ken Marshall (Polytechnic CC) to their number (the rabbit analogy begins to build). Between them the three men now had four bikes and they decided to loan the spare out on rote to any cycling serviceman on leave in Cairo who might fancy joining them for the odd ride. This information was posted in the English language newspaper *Egyptian Mail* and immediately letters began pouring in from cyclists eager to have their names added to the growing list. So great was the response that the *Mail's* sports editor, Arthur Barber, wrote a special feature which in turn, to Johnnie's amazement, elicited an even larger response, this time from right across the Middle East, Algiers to Baghdad, 180 letters in all representing every rank in the army, navy and air force. At this point Johnnie realised how much cyclists on active service were missing the fellowship of the wheel and he decided to organise a reunion in Cairo with the object of forming a club.

Over a hundred enthusiastic wheel-folk crowded the hall. They came from all parts of the Middle East. Many had special leave and travelled down from Palestine. Others hitchhiked from lonely desert airfields and camps. All the services corps and regiments were represented and the Eight Army crusader flash was prominent. (*Avon Advertiser.*)

The first item on the agenda was the choice of a name. As the club was to have no rules and no membership fee, someone suggested Buckshee (from the Arabic word *baksheesh* meaning 'free' or 'something for nothing') and so the name finally adopted was 'The Fraternity of the Buckshee Wheelers'. Paddy Roebuck, in giving the toast, said:

This club began with two clouds of dust in the Delta, two clouds which never seemed to meet. One was me and the other Johnnie Walker. We had a few rides together and soon a few others joined us – until on last Sunday's run we got together twelve people.' (*Avon Advertiser*)

So now they had a club and a name, but only one spare bike. The problem was solved by an appeal to Britain's cycle manufacturers back home. Again the response was far greater than anything Johnnie had foreseen. One day three large army wagons filled to the brim with a hundred brand new bicycles rolled up outside General Staff

Intelligence in Cairo. These, too, like the club were *baksheesh*. But now Johnnie faced another problem – where to store this newly acquired largesse. Fortunately, his friend Paddy Roebuck had a cellar ('Paddy's dug-out') in one of the less salubrious districts of the city and here they remained until arrangements could be made to dispatch them in batches to branches of the Wheelers that had been formed right across the Middle East, in places as far apart as Jerusalem, Iraq, Syria and Algiers.

Now they had a club, name and bikes. But where, if necessary, could essential basic spares be found if required in a hurry? The answer comes in a contemporary prize-winning letter published in *Cycling*. There, RAF man L.A.C. Statter painted a vivid picture of Bellouni, a Cairo cycle dealer. He was of mixed Egyptian and Italian descent, his advertisements being tri-lingual to include English. His shop in the native quarters is described as 'the Mecca of all spares-hunting Middle East cyclists' and 'though the front of the shop is barely eight feet. across, its dim recesses stretch farther back than anyone has ever been known to penetrate. Bicycles of every type and nationality hang from the ceiling like stalactites.' Statter comments on Bellouni's unfailing Oriental courtesy: '... the purchase of valve rubber or half a dozen spokes being always attended by a glass of coffee, the offer of a cigarette and a display of the Eastern "all-the-time-in-the-world" attitude.'

The casual chaos that surrounded Bellouni's dealings will surprise no one who experienced the small British cycle shop of that era: 'The search for a piece of notepaper necessitates the emptying of all his pockets, stuffed with paper money, old bills and bits of chalk; and the search is renewed and his money strewn all over the place again every time he needs a match for the inevitable Egyptian cigarette.' I well remember Jim Wilson of Wilson's Cycles, Sheffield (reputed to sell more light bulbs than cycle spares) turning his shop upside down to find an invoice: 'I know I've got it here somewhere, kid!' scratching his head with workshop-greasy fingers. And just like Chez Jim and other UK counterparts, this shop kept the wheels of commerce turning with a crude form of hire purchase: 'With "the crazy English" he is surprisingly tolerant, for he takes no note of army numbers or postal addresses if there is an item on the book, [but] he is very seldom let down by the club folk out here.' The letter concludes: 'Such a shop is very useful to clubmen at present stationed in the Middle East. Without it they could hardly continue their sport.'

The next step for Johnnie, Paddy and the committee was to organise a race. It was to be a 25-mile time trial held in October 1941, starting at the pyramids and heading out into the desert with a dead turn at the twelve and a half miles point in the road. Unfortunately, on the day appointed, the weather was unusually bad. A *kamsin* (sandstorm) blew up, blocking out the sun, and the riders were blinded and lacerated as they strove to force a passage across the desert into the gale-force wind. Groups of Arabs squatting at the roadside in the shelter of their camels must have shaken their heads in disbelief as, one by one, these 'mad-dog English' battled past, heads down into the storm. Corporal Eric Mustill (East Liverpool Wheelers), normally a 63-minute man, won in a time of 92 minutes, his slowest ever (in later years he would describe it as 'the ride of my life'). He was presented with the Bully Beef Trophy. This had been created by a cyclist working in Royal Ordnance and consisted of a silver plated bully beef tin mounted on a plinth and hammered into a pyramid shape.

Meanwhile the war had become bogged down in stalemate in the Western Desert. Men on leave from the front line in Cairo would join in with the regular Sunday club runs, which usually took place where the Nile splits in the flat delta region. A cutting from the *Egyptian Mail* gives a flavour of what might be expected:

A typical run with Buckshee Wheelers means about 100 miles, despite the heat and bad roads. Delta Barrage, that surprising wonderland of green fields and gracious trees in the midst of sand and sun-baked hills, is their favourite halt. The main roads, metalled, are terrible, but the dirt roads that run alongside the irrigation ditches are quite smooth riding.

This club run would be a highlight for those men on furlough about to return to their battle stations – sadly, for these young heroes to whom we owe our freedom today, this might well turn out to be their last bike ride. A favourite route was on the road running beside the Sweet Water Canal, which, according to Johnnie, was an open sewer that smelled anything but sweet.

Johnnie was a great raconteur and one of these club runs figures amongst his favourite stories. One blistering hot day as they were cycling along in a temperature of 120 degrees Fahrenheit and overtaking a camel train, one of the beasts took fright and, swinging round with its pannier bag, barged a rider off the road and into the Sweet Water. He was fished out and dried off. But in the heat, the dreadful stench of excrement emanating from his clothing was more than anyone could bear. 'Sorry, old boy, but you're going to have to ride alone.' And so he did for the rest of the day, well downwind, several lengths off the back.

If anyone wanted to test their fitness, they could take up the 120-mile Falam and back challenge (similar, Johnnie said, to the Sheffield–Cleethorpes–Sheffield challenge). This was almost entirely across empty desert.

The success of the Bully Beef 25 led in 1944 to the decision to hold a 50-kilometre massed start race on the aristocratic island of Ghezira. Permission was granted by the chief of police, Russell Pasha, to close the roads with the provision of several hundred policemen to keep the 13-lap course free of traffic. Faris Bey Sarafin, a rich Egyptian anglophile sportsman, former Oxford graduate and cricket blue, donated a magnificent silver cup costing fifty guineas, but the troops quickly nicknamed his beautiful Sarafin Trophy 'The Paraffin Lamp'. As before, entries poured in, 120 in all, including the local Egyptian champion. All that was missing were sets of jerseys in various club colours to help identify the riders. Once again Johnnie called for help on Army Ordnance where a section was given over to manufacturing flags and pennants for tanks, armoured cars, staff cars and ceremonial occasions. This production line now switched entirely for a whole week to manufacturing 120 racing jerseys in the colours of the participating clubs.

All this time, in his dealings with the military top brass, Johnnie had bluffed his way through. The officers he dealt with never questioned his authority, always assuming that he had permission for whatever he proposed from someone higher up in the chain of command, and without ever actually resorting to lies he managed to maintain this illusion. He must have exuded an air of total trustworthiness, as Victor Selwyn, editor of the Salamander Trust *Oasis* poetry magazine, illustrates:

> He was a man who enjoyed the distinction of being the only one to whom Randolph Churchill would entrust the key of his drinks cupboard, being wary of the Fleet Street exiles who staffed GSI.

But now he almost came unstuck. The Grand Prix de Ghezira, with its road closures, figured as such a big event in the daily life of Cairo that he proposed to play it safe – go right to the top and get a permit from the area commander Brigadier Crystal, whilst at the same time asking him to start the race in the belief that this would more easily bring the Big Cheese on side. At the meeting where this was agreed was a journalist from the *Mail*, who unfortunately jumped the gun. Before any approach had been made to the mighty Brigadier, a banner headline appeared in the next day's newspaper: '*Brigadier Crystal to start cycle race!*' Of course, at this stage, the Brigadier knew nothing of the plan and on reading the newspaper blew his top. He ordered his ADC to bring the officer i/c Buckshee Wheelers into his presence. The problem was that the Wheelers were not organised on army lines and there was no officer i/c; if anyone was in charge of this DIY *baksheesh* outfit it was Johnnie himself, but he was a mere staff sergeant and the Brigadier refused point blank to meet with an NCO. The ADC informed Johnnie in no uncertain terms, 'You'll have to find an officer from somewhere or there's no chance whatsoever of the race going ahead.'

The only bicycling commissioned officer in Cairo at that time was Alex Josey, Polytechnic CC, a former assistant editor of *Cycling*, and now an RAF Flight Lieutenant. Without disclosing the gravity of the situation Johnnie said, 'Look, Alex, old chap, Brigadier Crystal has asked to speak to an officer – just a few questions he wants to put, you understand, a few loose ends to tie up, won't take more than a couple of minutes.'

Alex duly attended upon the fiery Brigadier, who had him standing to attention for twenty minutes whilst he ranted and raved. What the hell did he think he was playing at? Who did the Buckshee Wheelers think they were anyway giving him orders through the pages of a newspaper – and so on and on? Finally, the despairing

Alex was dismissed. Wan-faced he saluted and turned to leave. As he reached the door, the Brigadier said, 'By the way, what time do you want me there?'

Racing in the desert

Andy Maund

107, M.U. R.A.F KASFAREET.

GRAND PRIX DE KASFAREET

Promoted by the

EXILES CYCLING CLUB

By kind permission of Group Captain W.D.J. Mickie.

50 KILOMETRE MASSED START CYCLE RACE

11 LAPS

Sun. April 1st. 1945.   Start 09.00 hrs.

Prizes Presented by Group Capt. W.D.J. Mickie.

SPECTATORS

Please keep off the rounds and give the riders a sporting chance.

OFFICIAL PROGRAMME: - **P.T. 1**

Proceeds to R.A.F. Benevolent Fund.

Andrew's Printing - Ismailia

As we all know, Rommel got his comeuppance at the hands of the Desert Rats in October 1942 at the Battle of Alamein. The Wermacht, utterly routed, had nowhere to retreat but into the hands of the Americans, who were to invade North Africa via Tunisia. It was a classic pincer tactic and, as Winston Churchill later remarked, the turning point of the war. By 1945 and VE Day, the Buckshee Wheelers had grown to 19 clubs.

The Exiles CC was also formed around the same time and became the Wheelers' chief rival in Cairo and Alexandria. Between them, they organised a full programme of racing (including an Australian pursuit and a hill climb up two kilometres of one-in-eight gradient, too much for many competitors who dropped out with heat exhaustion). One highlight was the annual track meeting held at the famous Alamein Club before 15,000 spectators, including many high-up service chiefs. The British Ambassador to Egypt, Lord Killearn, presented the prizes. Interestingly, in all these events, Egyptians, Syrians and Armenians were allowed to join with British servicemen. In the broad fraternity of cycling there was no apartheid.

Much like British clubs back home, the Wheelers upheld the tradition of the annual reunion or club dinner. L.A.C. Browning (Ringwood CC) acted as on-the spot and forces-radio commentator at most of the races and post war at Herne Hill track meetings – a very fine after-dinner speaker he was too, according to contemporary press reports – and I am indebted to his daughter Rosemary for the loan of material from the family archive, which includes two autographed dinner menus, one held at the Freemason's Hall, Cairo in September 1943, and the other at Kubri Camp in December 1944. Beside each guest's signature a home club appears, confirming that the membership was drawn from all over the British Isles. The Kubri five-course menu would have had the ration-hit folks back home salivating: soup, fried lemon sole, roast loin of lamb with mint sauce and roast potatoes, fruit tart and cream, cheese and biscuits and coffee. No food shortages here! (Was this proof, perhaps, of Johnnie Walker's sway extending beyond royal army ordinance to catering and the quartermaster's store?) Bottom left of the menu card appears the single word 'Bar'. How the amber liquid must have flowed.

One facet of service life was a zany sense of humour that took many forms (for example, the 'Paraffin Lamp') and was still around after the war in the 1940s and 50s, especially amongst the national servicemen that I served with. The printed menu for the 1943 Cairo

Reunion is a good example. This time there are six courses, all with a cycling flavour: Bardin soup, filled tubular and Ellimans Athletic, Roast Saddle of Brooks or stewed Alpaca with derailleur potatoes and spring links, Russian Charlotteville, Bukra fa mish-mish and fruit juice or Emprote. The joke has long since lost its contemporary relevance and I had to do some research to bring it to life. Ellimans is an embrocation to soothe aches and pains and was much used by cyclists as a pre-race warm-up cream; Brooks is a famous saddle manufacturer; alpaca is a woollen cloth used to make the windproof jackets that were then standard cycling wear; a spring link connects the two ends of a chain; Emprote was the trade name for an 'energy' food preparation that was a mixture of dried milk and cereal; Charlotte Russe was a popular dessert with basic ingredients of sponge fingers and custard and the famous Charlotteville CC, founded in 1903, was a Guildford club widely represented amongst the Wheelers; Bardin and Bukra fa are probably references to things Egyptian that would have raised a laugh amongst the servicemen at the dinner, but are now lost to us (Ansata Bint Bukra is a line of Egyptian race horses and 'mish-mish' is slang for mishmash, suggesting this otherwise nameless dish might be connected with a horse's backside. I speculate!) One diner (Ned Horn or 'Homo?') has signed himself in as from 'Gravesend Puffs'.

I like to think this earthy humour came out of the music hall tradition (as did 'The Old Bazaar in Cairo' and sand dance featured in 'Itinerants') and found its way into the many popular post-war radio comedy shows like ITMA and Much Binding in the Marsh and The Goons. The humour was broad and sometimes suggestive, though never OTT, and was often marked by catch-words or phrases that the vast radio audiences listened out for, recognised and afterwards repeated with glee to their friends in public. (Examples: 'Can I do yer now, sir?' Mrs Mop, or 'When I was in Sidi Barani – the boastful officer-bore in Much Binding. My characters, Tiny, Joe and Widget, are not untypical of this trend to show off the fact that one was intelligently 'with it'). During the dark days of war, it boosted morale and helped to keep spirits up, so much so that many people of my generation, including cyclists, claim they were never happier. Since then, that all-pervading spirit of 1950s'optimism has been much satirised. (Ay, we were poor but we were 'appy! – Nay, lad, we were 'appy *because* we were poor!')

A rich vein of this optimism alongside a determination to make the best of a bad job runs through the newspaper cuttings I have read in preparing this account. There would have been little understanding or sympathy for the authors of our modern-day misery memoirs, who would have been told in no uncertain terms to 'stop blubbing and get on with it.'

Even though far from home and in a war zone, the Wheelers did not escape the controversy that had split British cycling. Strong differences of opinion must have existed privately from 1942 onwards when Stallard promoted his Llangollen-Wolverhampton massed start race on open roads in defiance of an NCU ban, but in the interests of unity they were kept under wraps until March 1945 when an interview with Johnnie Walker in *Air Force News* opened up the floodgates. Johnnie made it absolutely clear that he was a fan of Stallard and the BLRC and this ran alongside an article by C R Potter attacking the NCU for keeping UK cycling in the dark ages. The editor of the *News* was astonished by the hornets' nest that this stirred up.

> The N.C.U. are sensitive souls, it seems, and the mail bag has been filled with their slings and arrows.

He was accused of ignorance or being a closet supporter of the BLRC. Naturally, he allowed right of reply, which came from Alex Josey, the Wheelers' president and 'assistant editor of *Cycling* for ten years, a councillor of the CTC, national Hon. Sec. of the Road Time Trials Council and an NCU judge.' Josey accused Walker and Potter of breaking a gentleman's agreement not to involve the Wheelers in politics. Clearly, he was a very big gun of the conservative cycling establishment back home and, unleashed, did not mince his words in condemning the League as 'just noisy little rebels.' He contrasted them with the NCU, 'a law-abiding and responsible organization which has controlled massed start racing and track racing for some 60 years.'

> The Home Secretary has stated that massed start cycle races on public roads constitute a danger to other road users. The Ministry of Transport says that these events shall not be held.
> Taking advantage of the war, however, a few hundred irresponsible cyclists broke away from the national organisations and they are holding these races in spite of the Government's edict against them. At the moment the Government is too busily occupied to do much about it, but action must come sooner or

later. – I was personally concerned at the beginning of the war with this unfortunate rebel movement and I tried hard to crush it in the interests of cyclists generally. – Time trials in England is (*sic*) our national cycling sport and has been for 40 years. More than a thousand racing cycling clubs were affiliated to the RTTC in 1939 and each club had an individual membership ranging from 20 to 200.

As for public interest, time trial sport is held more or less secretly in the early hours of the morning on the highways in order not to inconvenience other road users. One of the RTTC regulations insists there should be no encouragement of spectators.

Massed start racing is a spectator sport and the riders love spectators. All riders start in a bunch and such races have been very successfully held under the auspices of the NCU on roads closed to the public.

Josey adds that the government and every cycling body in the UK 'are all opposed to these noisy little rebels who, in our absence, may possibly wreck the sport at home.' He has backing in a letter from LAC Bunn of RAF Aboukir headed 'Potter's Nonsense':

This rebel organisation composed largely of raw youngsters promote mass start races on public roads contrary to NCU rules and against Home Office ruling. Their sole aim is to ape the Continental rider, with all the 'flash' rig of these roadmen.

Doubt surrounds the accuracy of Josey's comments on the Home Secretary and Ministry of Transport. Even Stallard would not have gone ahead in the face of explicit government opposition. It seems likely these are the RTTC's own views as expressed to the Ministry of Transport and not the Government's. Why, if the Government felt so strongly, did they take no action; write to chief constables, for example? Also Josey refers to 'this unfortunate rebel movement' as being in existence at the 'beginning of the war' i.e. 1939. The BLRC wasn't formed until 1942. 'Flash rig' indicates the RTTC's puritanical hatred of Continental racing.

The editor comments, 'That's a fair show for the blue-eyed boys of the NCU – they don't like being called venerable gents, remember.' To restore the balance, he throws in two letters from BLRC supporters. LAC Poulter writes:

Congratulations to Johnnie Walker and C R Potter for his article. This was great stuff. The only criticism I have to make is that his attack on the NCU was not strong enough. Many people don't realise how much harm this organisation has done to the prestige of British cycling throughout the Continent. If it were not for the spirit of some of the racing cyclists themselves, competition from Britain would be almost non-existent. Small wonder that they formed their own league. The NCU, I feel, have a real kick coming to them.

LAC Black of Heliopolis agrees, asserting that Johnnie's opinion was that of the majority of cyclists in the Middle East. Presumably he has in mind those races promoted at reasonable hours of the day in front of spectators and on open roads when he says, 'The Buckshee Wheelers have shown what cycling can be. Britain would lead in cycling if it were not for the dead hand of the NCU .'

Following the success of the Buckshee Wheelers, cyclists serving in other theatres of war formed their own cycling clubs: The Jungle Roamers in Ceylon, The Central Mediterranean Wheelers in Italy, The Tropical Twiddlers in India, The Liberation C. C. in Europe to name the foremost.

As a serviceman's organisation, it was not expected to survive when the British finally quit Egypt altogether in 1953. But true to the spirit of camaraderie forged in those difficult years, the Wheelers have continued to hold their annual reunion and Dinner with a re-run next day of the Bully Beef 25 (now with a nod towards the ever-increasing age of the membership, reduced to 25 kilometres).

The Wheelers first really came to my attention in 1954 when I was doing my national service at RAF Stafford. By this time with British forces out of Egypt and membership closed, the Bully Beef 25 and the Grand Prix de Ghezira had been repatriated to Britain. Whilst the 25 was reserved for the members only, the massed start race, added to the Army Cycling Union calendar, was thrown open to cyclists from all three branches of the armed forces. It was held for the first time on open roads in and around the 7000 acres site of Porton Camp in Dorset in 1951 and won by Peter Proctor. In 1952, Bernard Pusey was the winner and in 1953 RAF man Gino Goddard (Kenton Road Club). In September 1954, it was an RAF Stafford one-two, Norman Purdy beating me in the sprint.

The author on the Derbyshire climb of Beeley Moor in the
Buckshee Wheelers' GP de Gezira, 1956

By 1956 the Grand Prix de Ghezira had become a completely open
event promoted by Sheffield Phoenix under League rules. That year I
went one better than on my previous attempt. The race was held over
a tough circuit on a cool, rainy day in the High Peak, far removed
from its original venue in steamy Cairo, and I managed to win the
uphill sprint finish in Chatsworth Park.

Returning to 'Civvy Street' after the war, Johnnie Walker settled back into club life. True to his principles, he resigned from the NCU-affiliated Sheffield Central for the BLRC Phoenix. He was a wonderful after-dinner speaker with a fund of amusing stories delivered in his own jaunty style reminiscent of General Montgomery addressing the troops. With his wife as stoker on their tandem he could often be seen out and about in the surrounding countryside. He will be best remembered, however, as the driving force behind the Buckshee Wheelers, an unofficial organisation that was contrary to all service regulations yet typically British in being run by amateur enthusiasts under almost impossible wartime conditions.

'Pasha' Browning at a Buckshee reunion

ITINERANTS

No self-respecting bike rider, out for a bash with the lads on what is euphemistically termed 'a club run', wants to be the first to cry mercy. Joe, nicknamed 'Uncle' for his Stalinist leanings, had suffered for an hour or more and bit his tongue. But enough was enough. With a turncoat autumn morning, frost preceding warm sunshine, and under his pure wool, turtleneck sweater and thick plus fours, perspiration trickled and dripped – he could bear it no more. 'I could kill for a pint,' he ventured, the plea utterly lost on his two chums, incommunicado in their half-wheeling land of the deaf. He drew deeper breath and bellowed: 'I SAID I COULD KILL FOR A PINT.'

Widget, battling at the front to keep abreast of Tiny, spared him no more than a backward glance. 'Just ten more miles. Your puncture set us back.' He was gasping. 'The club awaits us at the Ranch House. We're late as it is.' But it was Tiny the Unpredictable who took pressure off the pedals.

'To hell with it!' he shouted. 'Shall we be slaves to any bloody club's timetable? We're Buckshee Wheelers, for Christ's sake. We do it our way.' Unclipping his pump, he began whirling it round his head like a claymore. 'My kingdom for a pint! Follow me, you brave warriors!'

With Widget outvoted, the pump pointed off down a tree-lined lane. The cool pint his holy grail, Tiny's twirling little legs stepped up the pace. Tumbled acorns and hazelnuts pinged as their wheels spun through crackling brown leaves. Then they came upon cottages with orange-glowing roofs and gardens ablaze with Michaelmas daisies, a steaming duck pond and there, at its rushy margin, an ancient half-timbered coaching inn sandwiched uneasily between church and church hall. Above the arched entrance hung a signboard from rusty chains. As they passed beneath, Widget glanced up to see a painted blacksmith, all muscle and brawn, bestriding his anvil. One arm brandished a hammer, the other circled the slim waist of a mermaid enthroned on his knee. The sullen couple scowled down imperiously as the wheeled intruders entered their domain.

In the cobbled yard behind the pub, two mares hitched to a rail beside a horse trough snorted in alarm as Tiny let forth a whoop. 'Welcome to the Mermaid and Anvil!' Balanced stationary, he rocked to and fro on his fixed wheel before vaulting athletically backwards over his saddlebag and catching his machine as it fell. He bowed.

'Good choice, O Tiny.' Uncle negotiated his huge bulk slowly to terra firma. 'I well recall this hostelry from days of yore. Best pint in Christendom.'

'Ay,' said Tiny. '1939 it was, and I can see it's not changed a jot. Good pubs like good mates, they never let you down. Put it there!' Grinning, they spat on their hands, like gipsies at a horse sale, and shook. Joe nodded at the two mares. 'Guess we just rode into town, eh pardner?'

'Sure guess we did.' To Widget's gross embarrassment, it was Tiny and Joe suddenly become Hopalong Cassidy. Together they turned and slouched like Wild West gunslingers, finger on the trigger, into the pub's gloomy interior, deliberately clacking their shoe-plates in unison on the bare floorboards. Here the would-be comedians halted to face each before launching into another of their toe-curling impersonations, this time of characters from the ITMA radio show.

'Can I do yer now, sir?'

'Don't forget the diver!'

Tiny fished to the lugubrious depths of his voice box. 'Funf has spoken,' he growled.

Laughing, the two show-offs turned to the bar for approval of their histrionic genius. But the landlord, lips pursed, was focused hard on polishing a beer glass.

'First pint's on me,' said Joe, undeterred. 'Good morgen, mein host. May it please thee to dispatch us three pints of thy foaming ale?'

'Stones bitter?'

'Ay, Stones's fighting brew,' Tiny chirruped.

With a grunt the landlord tossed Joe's coins into the till.

The good ale from the bar had a sobering influence on the jocularity of the thirsty ones, who now turned their attention to a rotund couple in jodhpurs and hacking jackets sitting at a cast-iron table. They were tucking into large plates of boiled ham and tomatoes. 'That's York ham, I'll warrant,' Tiny whispered, his sharp little nose aquiver with anticipation. 'Home-cured York ham cut fresh from the bone and a pint of Stones! O Mother! Food and drink for the gods! What say you, gentlemen? Shall it be three platefuls of the similar?'

Agreement was instantaneous. With strict food rationing in place, the chance of such a culinary treat wasn't to be ignored. Even Widget had to admit it took precedence over a ten miles ride to meet up with the club. The order was laid and six shillings rattled into the landlord's till. They sat at a gnarled, bacon-back pew under a pair of nicotine-yellowed hunting prints.

'Well, I suppose you're to be congratulated, Tiny,' Widget grudgingly admitted. 'I had my doubts back there, but this sure beats Ranch House grub.'

'Ay, it's years since I tasted real York ham,' said Joe, 'Pity them poor sods. It'll be soggy chips and iron-crust pie for them.'

'Pie'll be off by now,' chuckled Tiny. 'Soggy chips and beans more like. They'll be green wi' envy when we tell 'em about this.'

'Green wi' food poisoning more like!'

Their hilarity was interrupted by the landlord's wife, a starved weasel of a woman with lank hair, carrying a tray of ham salads, sliced bread and thin spindles of margarine. She banged these down onto the table together with a jar of salad cream and without a word stalked back towards the kitchen.

Widget perceived something was amiss. 'Excuse me,' he called after her. 'To save your feet, would you care for me to collect the cutlery?' Without a backward glance, she disappeared through the door.

'Capable woman like her don't need help from a fellow that can't vault off his bike,' chuckled Tiny.

'Be patient,' said Joe. 'Confucius he say, all things come to he who waits.'

And so they waited. They waited as the big hand of the wall clock crawled past twelve. They waited another five minutes. Seven! At twelve ten, they were still waiting, staring ravenously at the untouched plates of succulent sliced ham and lovely sweet tomatoes. But the cutlery did not materialise.

Uncle Joe could bear the torment no longer and clumped up to the bar. The landlord was busy serving one of the smoke-filled front rooms and through the drift of jovial chatter came the thump of darts and clicking dominoes. Someone tinkered Nelly Dean on an out-of-tune piano. The man returned bearing an armful of empties. 'Excuse me,' said Joe, 'your good lady appears to have forgotten our cutlery.'

'Oh no, she hasn't.'

'Evidently she has.' Joe indicated the table. 'See, no knives, no forks.'

'Oh no, she hasn't.' The landlord carried on rinsing the beer jugs.

'But she has!' insisted Joe. It was becoming like an Xmas pantomime, that is until the landlord thrust a grubby, handwritten menu under his nose and pointed to the bottom line. Puzzled, Joe brought it to the table. 'Here, have a shufti. What do you make of this?'

'Has to be a joke!' exclaimed Widget.

'Is it a joke?' Tiny demanded of the landlord, now leaning hands-clasped across the bar.

'Do I look like a joking man?'

His granite-like face made it hard to disagree. 'Like it says, "Cutlery provided at the establishment's discretion or otherwise upon deposit".'

'I don't understand. What does it mean, "discretion"?'

'It means I decide who I entrust with my precious antique knives, forks and spoons.'

'You mean we have to pay a deposit for our cutlery?'

'Not your cutlery, *my* cutlery.'

Widget was aghast. 'But why? They've got cutlery.' He indicated the equestrian couple. 'Have they paid a deposit?'

'Well, unless them horses out there are penny farthings in disguise, they aren't pedal cyclists.'

'Pedal cyclists? What's that got to do with it?'

'That's for me to know and you to guess.'

The landlord's sarcasm was riling Tiny even more than the absence of cutlery and he suddenly burst forth, 'Look here, Adolf, that's discrimination. You can't discriminate against us because we're cyclists. We just fought a bloody war to stop all that.'

'Don't you dare call me Adolf.' Now the landlord was aghast. 'And don't you talk to me about discrimination. I'll tell *you* all about discrimination, young man. Discrimination is when you cyclists come into my pub and nick my cutlery. That's discrimination!' And with that the landlord squashed the wasp of discrimination flat on the bar with his big ham-fist.

'Cyclists?' Widget tried to reason. 'How come? Cyclists are no more thieves than normal people. Not us, at any rate. We've not visited this establishment in eight years and nicking cutlery isn't our forte. Please don't tar everybody with the same brush. We're honest as the day is long.' His companions nodded, crossing their fingers under the table. 'Now be fair, sir, we've paid for our meal in good faith, so you must give us some cutlery to eat it with.'

'Don't you must me!' the landlord yelled, reddening. 'I know the law. This is an inn so I can't turn you away during opening hours, much as I might like. Ale, yes. Vittles, yes. But cutlery is entirely at my discretion.' He tapped his chest to emphasise the point. 'Cyclists,' he went on, 'is in my experience not to be trusted. They come in here puddlin' my floors wi' rain off their capes, buy half a shandy and sit for hours, nattering. My customers have reported seeing 'em out there mending their punctures in my horse trough, without so much as by y'r leave, using my spoons and forks for tyre levers. And my expensive hallmarked and engraved cutlery, what I can't replace due to the steel shortage and what's part of my pre-war heritage, keeps going missing.' He paused for several deep breaths to overcome the pain of his loss before concluding, 'With the deepest respect, I have to say to you that cyclists is a shifty lot! And they're untraceable. They come from God only knows where and go back same place. They're – (he struggled to find the right word) – they're itinerants!"

'Itinerants?' Tiny was by now beside himself with rage. 'Do you mean gypsies?'

'If the cap fits, wear it!'

'I've been called some things in my life, but never an itinerant.'

He leapt up from his seat and addressed the landlord with all the authority his five feet two inches of quivering manhood could muster.

'I am a Desert Rat,' he asserted.

'Ay, me too, ' said Joe. 'We're Desert Rats, all of us, and Buckshee Wheelers and proud of it.'

'What they mean is they *were* Desert Rats,' Widget hastily amended, thinking his friends were about to resort to fisticuffs. 'That was during the war when we fought the Hun in Egypt. It's what Jerry called us because we took shelter from their guns in foxholes – like rats. But in the end we showed 'em and won the war and now we're civilians again. We're all civilians. Let's just remember that, gentlemen, please, and behave civilised.'

'Aye, we deserve to be treated civil,' said Joe, unrequited. 'It was us ran Rommel out of North Africa to save civilisation and we won't be beat by a bigot back home.'

It was a proud boast. But, as Widget perceived, they were beaten. Nothing short of a deposit was going to alter the landlord's mind. He was smirking at his wife, who, roused by the commotion, stood framed in the kitchen doorway, holding a carving fork and dustbin-lid shield, the very image of Britannia militant. 'It's all right, my love,' he cooed. 'The war's over, you can go back to work.' Assured of his triumph, he turned away to serve the other rooms and Widget pulled his comrades back to their seats.

'Perhaps we should offer him that deposit?' he suggested, ever the peacemaker.

'Not on your Nelly,' said Tiny. 'It's discrimination and a damned insult to the whole cycling clan and we shouldn't be party to it.'

Jo agreed. 'No backing down. Remember the Spanish battle cry? *'No passaran!* The fascists shall not pass'. Chamberlain gave in to Hitler and look where that led.'

But short of backing down and paying up there seemed no way out. They sat gloomily contemplating their plates, hunger gnawing at their empty bellies. Finally, Tiny reached for a tomato, but Widget restrained him. 'Only common Arabs eat with their fingers,' he admonished. 'Remember, in Cairo, when we dined like aristocrats?'

'With Faris Bey Sarafin and that posh lot?'

'Ay, the finest of silverware, not to mention the lovely grub. Wait, I've got an idea.'

He dashed outside and returned with his tool kit. The tools, bandaged in an old greasy rag that doubled as a hand wipe, were tumbled onto the table – a medley of screwdrivers, tyre levers and spanners. 'I'll be blowed if we're beat,' he said. 'This isn't exactly cutlery, but we can make do and hold our heads up high. Tuck in, gents.'

By way of example, he chose a screwdriver as his fork and sawed at the ham with a tyre lever. Joe followed suit. Tiny was left with a tyre lever and a cone spanner. The cone spanner proved excellent for spreading margarine, but when he bit into the bread his teeth ground on something gritty and swallowing he suffered a coughing fit.

'Damnation!' he spluttered, much to the amusement of the two equestrians, who were relishing the whole spectacle.

Fate seemed to have set its face against them. Joe doused his ham with salad cream making it so slippery that, without the secure pinion of a fork, it skidded off the plate, down his trousers and onto the floor. He wiped his flies with the greasy rag, but this made a bad stain worse – and when he retrieved the ham from the floor, it was speckled with unwholesome dirt, rendering it inedible.

Widget sawed ineffectively at his tomato for a full minute with the tyre lever. In desperation he stabbed it with the screwdriver. It burst and spurting juice drenched his sweater.

The rumpus, meanwhile, had attracted the attention of one of the locals, peering into the back room from over the front bar. He called to his mates and soon a half dozen of them, already the worse for drink, began catcalling as the cyclists strove to come to terms with their lunch.

Far from subduing his obstreperous clientele, the landlord suggested they take a closer look at the 'itinerants' whose appalling behaviour had run to the insult of labelling him 'Adolf'. So they all trooped round to the back room, and made a raucous half circle in front of the chums' table.

'Hooligans!' yelled the fiery Tiny, spilling a mouthful of ham and bread down his sweater.

The rosy-faced yokels fell about laughing upon hearing his city accent. ''Ooligans!' they mocked. 'Ooly ooly 'ooligans!'

'This is like being in the stocks,' thought Widget and said so.

'I'll tell you what it's like,' said Joe. 'It's like being captured by Ities.'

'Ities never captured anyone except Abyssinians,' said Tiny.

'Exactly!' said Joe. 'That's exactly what I mean.' Though what he did mean was far from clear.

All might yet have ended peacefully, Widget realised later, had not Tiny at that moment stabbed his own tomato with a tyre lever. It flew off his plate onto the floor and immediately became the subject of a football scrum that ended with the tipsy farmhands barging into the table and spilling Stones's fighting brew over its occupants. Worse, somebody booted the squashed tomato and it hit Tiny on the forehead. The juice temporarily blinded him.

'Goal!' The youths were jubilant. Tiny rubbed his stinging eyes and vowed vengeance. The uproar brought more people clustering in from the front bar.

Then, to Widget's amazement, Joe levered himself up onto the pew. He stood there foursquare and solid, like some preposterous Victorian statue in his stained jersey and plus fours. Spilled beer dripped off his sleeves and made little ragged pools on the floor. He was preparing, Widget realised with dismay, to address the mob as if it was one of his Communist party meetings. For a moment height lent him tactical advantage and a tense silence descended on the room.

'Friends, countrymen,' he bellowed, words half remembered, perhaps, from some school play – comrades, lend me your ears. I come – that is, I mean – I'm here – ' He mumbled to a halt. The array of leering boozy faces, more menacing now they were attentive, had locked his tongue.

Oh for a magic carpet, Widget prayed, to whisk us away to the Ranch House. As if in answer to the prayer, Uncle suddenly rediscovered his voice.

'Fair do's!' he shouted. 'I'm here to ask you for fair do's! Nothing more. We've paid for our meal in honest coin and we should've knives and forks to eat it without the shame of a deposit. Isn't that what you'd expect for yourselves, comrades, fair do's?'

The 'comrades' appeared somewhat baffled by this unaccustomed show of rhetoric from an itinerant, but playing the game was something not entirely foreign to their natures. They began to shuffle and look a little sheepish. Widget was heartened to note a few heads nodding in support, even a burst of applause from a group of buxom wives in their Sunday best gathered at the back of the room. Encouraged, even intoxicated by his success, Joe continued, disastrously as it turned out.

'What the landlord here has done is probably against the law. He's no right to discriminate against pedal cyclists.' More nods of agreement and even some 'here heres'. 'It's against the codes of decency and hygiene – leastways, it would be in Soviet Russia where they do things rather better in the way of customer protection than we do in England.'

'Oh no!' Widget groaned, but the damage was done.

'Soviet Russia?' A farmer in gaiters voiced his distaste. 'What's he on about?'

'He says the Ruskies are better'n us,' said his companion.

'Are they buggery!'

'It's a damned lie!' someone else snarled amidst the rising groundswell of indignation. 'We can beat them Ruskies at football any day.'

'Ay, that's right, an' it was us and good old Churchill won the war for 'em too.'

Joe tried to explain it was just a matter of hygiene and decency, but reason's sworn foes, patriotism and xenophobia, were snapping at his size-twelve leather cycling shoes.

'Get off to Russia if yer don't like it here!'

'Ay, Bolshie bastards! Piss off!'

'Communist agitators, that's what you are!'

A storm was brewing and Widget perceived the moment had come to retire. Dragging the still expostulating Joe down from the pew, he joined Tiny in a hasty backs-to-the-wall retreat to the door, leaving their half-eaten meals on the table. Outside in the yard, the mob followed, booing and cursing. Their saddlebags were kicked, Widget's tools flung after him and he had to scrabble ignominiously in the muck and straw to pick them up off the cobbles. Then as they rattled out under the archway, some of the drinkers' squatting children rose up and pelted them with whatever came to hand.

As they fled, Widget perceived the landlord standing at the front entrance, waving a serviette in mock farewell.

They cycled for a mile or more, grim-faced and smarting – then the recriminations began.

'Brilliant!' said Tiny to Joe. 'You were brilliant! All that Communist claptrap, just perfect for the occasion!'

'I never said anything about Communism. Anyway, even if I had, a man's got a right to express his political opinion and tell the truth as he sees it,' insisted Joe. 'It's a free country. It just slipped out.'

'Slipped out! Might just as well have waved your Party card!'

'You've some room to talk, Tiny. Whose idea was it to go there in the first place? Not mine. And if you'd not been so uppity with that landlord, calling him Adolf, we might have won him over.'

'Rubbish!' snapped Tiny. 'Won him over! That slavering Schikelgruber!'

'Shurrup, both of you!' Widget, angry and baffled, had had enough. If they'd followed him and gone to the Ranch House, none of this would've happened. 'Arguing'll get us nowhere. Like they say, don't get mad, get even. We've been wronged, right? So let's do something about it.'

He rode on. The others followed behind in single file.

The nearby town smelled tantalisingly of Sunday roast as they cycled through its streets, empty save for a stray canine snuffling the gutter. Shadowy behind the taverns' frosted glass windows stood the Sabbath regulars, hands locked on their pints. Widget stopped outside a building with a blue lamp over the entrance. They stacked their bikes up against an iron railing and went inside.

Behind the counter a portly police sergeant was sitting, waistcoat unbuttoned, snoozing under the great weight of the *News of the World*. He jumped in alarm when Widget punched the bell.

'We've been assaulted, insulted – yes, and cheated,' Widget began. The sergeant gaped, his Sunday lunchtime idyll disrupted by this manifestation of stained and besmirched cyclists. Thank heavens, Widget thought ironically, that Justice is blind.

He recounted the whole story, leaving out only Joe's references to Soviet Russia.

The sergeant listened attentively, but as Widget's woeful tale ended offered little more than sympathy. 'Bad luck! But it's none o' my business. Withholding cutlery without deposit is unmannerly, but not a crime. Unfortunately, there's nothing we can do.'

'Nothing?'

'No, this is a civil matter between you and the landlord. It's very, very complicated. It's to do with contracts and whether they've been broke. It's a suing job, job for a solicitor.'

'A solicitor? That sounds expensive.'

'Justice doesn't come cheap. Take my advice. Forget it. Go somewhere else for a pint and a sarny, then hop on your bikes and buzz off home. You'll be none the worse for it tomorrow.'

It was tempting and Widget, left to his own devices, might have consented. But – 'Isn't there somebody could advise us today?' It was Tiny, feeling his honour as a Desert Rat and Buckshee Wheeler was on the line.

'Today?' The sergeant considered. 'Well, as a matter of fact, if you must insist, there is someone I know of who's expert in the field of law, but I can't guarantee he'll give you a good reception – it being Sunday like.'

The person in question, it transpired, was a retired judge. He had once had a reputation for hanging and flogging, but on quitting the bench had ingratiated himself locally by setting up stall at summer fetes as 'The Legal Beagle', offering his advice in return for a donation to his favourite charity, Conservative Party funds.

To Widget, it didn't sound promising.

'You reckon his charity might stretch to us?' asked Tiny hopefully.

'Who knows,' shrugged the sergeant. 'Depends on how you play your cards. It might be worth a try.'

The judge resided in a large ivy-clad, battlemented mansion on the edge of town. Haughty stone unicorns guarded the gate, and peacocks, rainbow in the sunlight, cried mournfully across its vast, empty lawns. The chums cycled tentatively up a long drive and heaped their bikes at the foot of some grand curving stone steps that mounted to a massive, brass-furnished door beneath a portico.

'Bit too toffee for my liking,' grumbled Joe.

'Then you'd better let me do the talking,' said Widget.

The bell jangled deep within the house and eventually the door creaked open to reveal a terrified housemaid. Was it their beery smell or Tiny's 'bloody' face or Joe's smeared flies? With a scream, she fled back down the hall. Voices yelped from the recesses and moments later she reappeared on the heels of a small red-faced, balding man bearing a billiard cue. To Widget, his bowed shoulders and firm stride suggested someone drawing a heavy sledge through thick snow. A hunter on the trail.

'Be off, you ruffians,' he yelled, brandishing the cue. 'I'll not tolerate beggars on my property!'

In a split second of brilliant intuition, Widget sprang to attention and roared, '7898363 Corporal Widget, SIR!' He saluted smartly.

'Permission to speak.'

The judge was somewhat taken aback. This was not the usual response of itinerants.

Pointing the thick end of the cue at Widget, he said, 'Well go on then. Out with it, man! Speak! I'll give you thirty seconds. But no funny business, mind.'

'We've come seeking justice, Your Honour.'

'Justice!' exclaimed the judge, as if he'd never heard the word before. 'Justice on a Sunday? Explain yourself.'

Once more Widget trotted out the prudently edited story of their suffering at the hands of the peevish landlord. The others only intervened to back him up with nods and grunts.

'Disgraceful!' exclaimed the judge when Widget had ended. 'All that good ham going to waste at a time of national shortage and austerity. The man deserves to be horsewhipped.' He brandished the cue again by way of illustration. 'Come in, come in. What are you standing there for?'

They followed him down the long hall into a drawing room hung with hunting trophies. 'Sit,' said the judge, and they perched themselves on the edge of a leather sofa under the baleful regard of a stuffed moose head. The maid reappeared with a tray of large glasses and proceeded to fill them with whisky and soda from the sideboard.

'Never knew a fighting man turn up his nose at a little snifter before combat,' the judge hooted. 'What unit were you with?'

'Seventh Armoured Division of the Eighth Army,' Joe said. "Desert Rats".'

The judge frowned. 'That socialist shite Montgomery, eh? Never mind, a soldier can't be blamed for his leaders.'

Joe was about to spring to Monty's defence until Widget kicked his ankle.

'Now, this landlord at the Mermaid. Know him very well. Never trusted him, though. Wouldn't be at all surprised if he watered the beer. However, he's done nothing criminal, in my opinion, withholding your cutlery. But there may be a civil case to answer: breach of contract. The supply of a meal assumes the supply of the means with which to consume it without deposit. I think that may well be your best avenue of redress, what?'

The chums heartily agreed, the whisky reviving their spirits and making all things seem possible.

'At present you have no case,' continued the judge, pacing the room and making imaginary golf swings with the cue. 'Leastways, you've got a case, but no witness, no reliable witness.'

'What about us?' Tiny asked. 'We witnessed what happened.'

'Ah yes, you,' said the judge. His penetrating blue eyes raked over them, and then he refilled their glasses. 'To impress a court, a witness must have pedigree and an honest face.'

Joe's indignation was about to burst forth, but again Widget kicked his ankle.

'In any case, the ideal witness should be independent. But don't worry, I have the very man for you – my man, in fact, Alfred.'

'But he wasn't there, this Alfred,' Widget protested.

'No, he wasn't. But he will be next time it happens. I have a plan. You're going to go back to that inn with Alfred and order another meal. When once again the cutlery isn't forthcoming, he will be your witness and speak out on your behalf in court.'

The chums looked at one another and smiled. Two stiff whiskies on an empty stomach and the stratagem seemed flawless. They thanked their host profusely and moments later were outside the front door again, awaiting the arrival of the pony and trap. His Honour stood with them on the steps, beaming. As Alfred flicked his whip and they mounted their bikes to follow behind, the judge saluted with a martial gesture of the cue. 'Good hunting!' he cried.

'He's a card!' Alfred exclaimed over his shoulder when they were out of earshot. 'He loves a wheeze – and the people he's hanged, you wouldn't believe how many. Sent 'em all down with a cheery "Good hunting!" Never bore none of 'em malice.'

Despite the heat of the day, Alfred's words sent a cold shudder down Widget's spine, and he continued to feel uneasy as the horse clopped along the short mile of country lane that brought them to the Mermaid and Anvil. They halted in the courtyard, dismounting slowly to delay the moment when they must once again face the choleric landlord and his tame mob.

The back room was deserted apart from a couple of solitary drinkers propping up the bar. All the action was once again up front in the packed saloon, where the landlord and his missus were busy serving in a hullabaloo of boozy singing.

What if he refuses to serve us, Widget wondered? Suppose he has us thrown out? What then?

But, to his surprise, when finally the landlord turned to check the back room, he gave no indication of animosity. It was quite remarkable, as though ejecting undesirables only to see them return within the hour was an everyday occurrence. He wiped his hands on a teacloth and presented himself.

They ordered beer and four ham and tomato lunches, paying up for Alfred, with sixpence extra for a dessert to accumulate the evidence. They occupied the same table. It had been righted and wiped clean, with all the spills cleared up but for a run of tomato juice on the glass of a hunting print to prove it had not all been a dream.

'All's well so far,' remarked Alfred, wiping the beery foam from his lips.

'Just you wait,' said Tiny, 'you'll see.'

They had not long to wait. The landlord's wife appeared through the kitchen door bearing a large tray. She placed a cut-glass jug of water with matching tumblers in the centre of the table. There followed freshly laundered serviettes rolled inside ivory rings, a silver plate condiment set, a bowl of toothpicks and – wonder of wonders – polished knives and forks of the finest quality, each stamped with a tiny mermaid and anvil motif.

They were still gaping when she came again with plates of ham and tomato, bread, butter (butter!), a cheese board with three choice cheeses and a cheese knife and a bowl of green salad and cucumber. The salad servers had porcelain handles decorated with pink roses and cherubs.

'I do hope you enjoy your meal,' she simpered before returning to the kitchen.

Widget was the first to speak. 'Well, I'm blowed. What d'you make of this?'

'Bit of all right, if you're asking me,' grunted Alfred through bulging cheeks.

At first the others couldn't bring themselves to eat. They sat and stared at the immaculate spread, hardly able to believe their eyes. This has to be a trick, thought Widget, and said so. Joe was more conciliatory. 'People have been known to repent of their wrongdoing,' he said. 'They often publicly confess to it in court in Mother Russia. Guilty conscience!'

'More like we've put the frighteners on him,' said Tiny, tucking in his serviette and cutting himself a slice of cheddar to accompany the tomato. 'Seeing me march back in here, he's thought: "Hi, hi, here comes trouble. Better treat 'em decently this time!"'

Widget discounted all these cosy explanations, but despite misgivings decided to say no more. He tucked in with the others and soon their plates were empty.

'Apple pie and custard, landlord' Tiny commanded with a haughty click of his fingers. The landlord disappeared into the kitchen, only to re-emerge with a message. It was for Alfred.

'His Honour's just 'phoned to say he wants you back at the mansion pronto.'

'Surely it can wait till I've had me pie,' Alfred protested.

But the landlord shook his head. 'He wants you now, urgent, and no messing.'

Evidently fearing for his job, Alfred bade them farewell.

The woman came in first to clear the table then distribute the steaming apple pies. Each was invisible under dollops of creamy custard that over-ran the plates and smelled deliciously of cinnamon.

The sight and scent of such fine fare had temporarily driven the purpose of the mission from Widget's mind. But it returned with a jolt when Joe suddenly exclaimed, 'Where's the spoons and forks?' Indeed, where were the spoons and forks? There were none. Also the serviettes, where were they? All disappeared with the landlord's wife.

Joe said quietly, 'I think we've been had.'

They sat and stared at the apple pies whilst the overflowing custard cooled and congealed before their eyes.

'Well,' said Widget, 'one thing's sure. I'm not going to demean myself by asking him, 'cos that's what he wants, to humiliate us again.'

'Well I will then,' exclaimed Tiny. 'Here, Adolf,' he shouted, banging on the table, 'we can't eat this. It's like soup. What about some spoons?'

75

The landlord had been contemplating them across the counter. Now a sly grin crossed his face. 'You know the house rules,' he said. 'I must have a deposit.'

'How come these "rules" didn't apply for our main course then?'

'You was with the judge's man, Alfred. He was your guarantee of good behaviour. Now he's gone, who knows what you might get up to? I'm not taking no more chances with my cutlery, leastways not without a very large deposit – say ten bob each?' He smirked. 'Failing that, I should eat your pie before it gets cold.'

The truth suddenly hit Widget between the eyes. 'This is a fix,' he exclaimed. 'You and that judge, you've set us up to make fools of us twice over.' He turned to the others. 'That Alfred said the judge enjoyed a wheeze. He was never intended to be our witness. Can't you see, it's all been a game? The judge and this landlord, they're having a laugh at our expense. He's been on the phone and they've set us up!'

'Don't know what you're on about,' said the landlord, 'but I can't imagine no judge being of assistance to itinerants, can you?' He exchanged a mirthful glance with his wife, standing arms akimbo in the kitchen doorway. 'Any road, comin' into my pub and showing off, treatin' me disrespectful, well now you're laughing t'other side of your faces.' He answered a call from the saloon bar.

'Bastards!' Tiny thumped the table so hard the plates leapt up in the air.

'Never trust a Tory,' declared Joe with grim satisfaction.

'Well, that's it,' snapped Tiny. 'I'm not hanging round here to be laughed at. I'm off. But first I'm gonna give Adolf here a good seeing to – and quite possibly his missus also, if she gets in my way. They've both led us a merry dance!'

'Hang on!' Widget pulled Tiny back down to his seat. 'Don't be so hasty. Violence 'll bring the whole pub down on us and we'll end up in court. What did you just say – about a merry dance?' Another brainwave had occurred to him. He drew Joe and Tiny into a huddle and began whispering.

'Well, what d'you think?' he concluded.

'It's absolutely crazy!' said Joe. 'But I'm game for it if he is.'

Tiny nodded. 'We've a right to be crazy, all we've been through. Count me in. Anything to get back at Adolf.' He went over to the bar where two tea towels had been draped to dry. 'These'll do for our heads.'

Widget arranged the tea towels loosely over the two men's hair and trailed them onto their shoulders. Then they removed their plus fours and stood in the centre of the room. Big Joe and diminutive Tiny made ridiculous figures beneath the red spotted tea towels, hairy calves and thighs exposed, shirt laps barely covering their backsides. Widget was hard put to withhold his mirth, recalling the two men's club dinner act that was always guaranteed to bring the house down. Now they would perform, not to please, but as a gesture of defiance.

The landlord had noticed something was afoot. 'Here, what's going on?' he bellowed, rushing to the bar. 'You can't strip off in here. It's against the law.'

At a signal from Widget, the two got into line, one leg slightly bent and forward of the other, as if to start a running race. Their bodies and heads were turned to the side, eyes wide open unblinking, one arm stretched out in front, the other behind, thumbs up, fingers pointed. Drumming out a rhythm with two beer jugs on the table, Widget began singing in a wavering high-pitched falsetto voice.

Sand bags, wind bags, camels with a hump,
Fat girls, thin girls, some a little plump,
Slave girls sold here, fifty bob a lump,
In the old bazaar in Cairo.

Brandy, shandy, beer without a froth,
Braces, laces, a candle for the moth ,
Bet you'd look a smasher in an old loin cloth,
In the old bazaar in Cairo.

Tiny and Joe began to dance, clacking their shoe plates in rhythm. It was the celebrated sand dance of Wilson and Keppel, a music hall parody drawn from ancient Egyptian tomb frescoes. They were well practised. Reaching the far wall, they turned in perfect formation and pranced back to the centre of the room.

'Stop!' screamed the landlord. They did. They bowed away from him, flipped up their shirt laps and mooned the full backside.

Harem, scarem, what d'ya think of that?
Bare knees, striptease, dancing on the mat,
Umpa! Umpa! That's enough of that,
In the old bazaar in Cairo.

The din had drawn some regulars and their womenfolk from the front bar. At first, they pointed, hooted and scoffed. But little by little, something of the anarchic spirit of the dance seemed to overcome them. Perhaps in response to a bet, and egged on by the hysterical cries of their womenfolk, four of the young men put handkerchiefs on their heads, kicked off their trousers and began jigging in a parallel line to Joe and Tiny. For first timers, Widget had to admit, they weren't at all bad, though reaching the wall their leader tripped over a chair and they all collapsed into a giggling, drunken heap.

Rice pud, very good, what's it all about,
Made it in a kettle and they couldn't get it out,
Everybody took a turn to suck it through the spout,
In the old bazaar in Cairo.

Now more and more began cramming into the room, clambering up onto the tables and pews to make space for the dancers. They clapped and hollered and stamped their feet in time to the dance. The vibration brought a tray of 'dead' glasses sliding off the bar and crashing to the floor where they were ground underfoot by heavy boots. Wave his arms and shout as he might, the landlord could not bring them to order. In fact, as Widget observed, the more alarmed he became, the more his excitement seemed to prompt others to break the bounds of propriety and join in the dance. Soon there were two sets of dancers, then three, all vying in bibulous absurdity – shoving, colliding, collapsing, reassembling, cavorting on, whilst at the centre Widget and Joe retained an icy, dignified professionalism, stepping with precise rude gestures and perfect concentration, seemingly oblivious to the growing chaos around them.

From the front room, the pianist struck up, cue for the audience, mainly of women, to add to the general racket with some raucous singing.

Then a lone, black-clad figure entered and pushed his way through the throng to the bar. He wore a dog collar. Flakes of whitewash, shaken from the ceiling, flecked his cassock. He began an altercation with the landlord. Both men gesticulated and shouted and Widget gathered that the Sunday School next door in the church hall was being interrupted by the commotion. The vicar pointed up at the clock. Of course! It was closing time.

Mamadan, Ramadan, everything in style,
Genuine beduine carpet with a pile,
Funny little odds and ends floating down the Nile,
From the old bazaar in Cairo.

The landlord clanged his closing bell repeatedly. It made no difference. This congregation couldn't hear, didn't want to. They were enjoying themselves far too much to be distracted by the trivia of licensing laws.

The vicar put his hand to his mouth and pressed back against the bar, aghast. In his rush to confront the landlord, he had missed one important detail, which now stared him in the face. Cavorting on the Sabbath like drunken savages was bad enough. But half naked! And in front of women! He stormed out.

The landlord fell to trying to preserve his property from the worst of misrule, gathering in as many jugs, glasses, plates and bottles as were not already trampled underfoot. He unhooked the pictures from the walls, steadied the oil lamps swinging on their chains – broken shades were devilishly expensive to replace. And then the vicar suddenly reappeared accompanied by the local bobby.

Widget watched as they stood in the doorway and the young constable, unsure how to proceed, adjusted his helmet and drew his truncheon – then, on second thoughts, thrust it back into its holster. An over made-up girl with bleached hair spun him round in a twirl. 'Come on, George, show us yer whistle!' He broke free and waved at the landlord, pointing to his watch, but poor 'Adolf' was too involved with redeeming his property to notice, especially since some dancers had now invaded the kitchen, from whence came a crashing of crockery as they clumsily sought to avail themselves of more tea towels.

The constable turned to the vicar and shrugged his shoulders. At this, the vicar went wild and, wagging his finger in the man's flushed face, lectured him on the theme of duty. The two men disappeared from Widget's view and he wondered if the constable was being persuaded to summon reinforcements. If a magistrate had to be called out to read the riot act on a Sunday, the consequences didn't bear thinking about. Perhaps now, having made their point, it would be a good time to beat a second retreat.

Events took the decision from his hands. The room suddenly emptied as everyone, save for Joe and Tiny, formed up into a conga line that took itself outside and around and around the courtyard.

Perhaps he feared losing his licence. Whatever the reason, Adolf now sped to where Widget was still beating out the rhythm and pleaded with him to leave.

Yashmaks, pontefracts, what a strange affair,
Dark girls, fair girls, some with ginger hair,
The rest of it is funny but they censor it out there,
In the old bazaar in Cairo.

Widget briefly paused. 'We usually charge a fee for entertainment.' The man hastened to the till and returned with a big, white fiver. Widget pinned it under one glass while he went on drumming with the other. 'We've had to cycle a very long way to get here. What about our expenses?' He sensed total capitulation. The landlord ran back to the bar, returning with a handful of silver. Widget stopped drumming and pocketed the money.

At a signal, Joe and Tiny metamorphosed into themselves and donned their plus fours. Widget took them by the hand and together they bowed low to the ashen landlord and his wife.

'Joe, Tiny and Widget – Desert Rats, Buckshee Wheelers and tuneful itinerants – ever at your service.'

As they mounted their bikes, the landlord, having locked the pub door behind them, was busy hurling pair after pair of trousers through the window.

Much later that day – one tearoom and a pub later, to be precise – they were still in celebratory mood as they tumbled out of The Rose and Crown and prepared for the ride home.

'A day to remember – better than demob – wait till we tell the club – nay, they'll never believe us. Eyup, Adolf's face when he come over all pleading – Funf has spoken!' Tiny did a little dance of surrender with his hands in the air. 'Kamerad!'

'You're pissed!' laughed Joe.

'Speak for yourself, Uncle, Supreme Leader of the Soviets!'

We're all pissed,' said Widget, 'and we deserve to be. We're celebrating the righting of a wrong.'

'We're celebrating fair do's.' Tiny made a megaphone of his hands and hooted at the full moon. The echo came back on the still, misty night air – 'Fair do's!'

'Hang about,' said Joe as they prepared to depart. 'My bike, it weighs an absolute ton.' He bounced the back wheel on the ground.

'More like your gut,' scoffed Tiny 'with all that ale you've just swilled.'

'No listen. There's something in my saddlebag.'

Indeed, when he dropped the rear wheel again, they heard a muffled metallic clattering. Joe undid the straps and lifted the flap. The moon glinted dully on something inside. Joe took it to the light of the oil lamp in the pub window. It was a dining fork.

'Look there.' Widget pointed to the handle and the tiny stamp of the Mermaid and Anvil.

Joe rummaged deeper in the bag and came up with both hands full of cutlery. 'Is this your idea of a joke, Tiny?'

'How could it be, comrade? I was performing with you, wasn't I. Must be Widget.'

'Not guilty,' said Widget. 'But I'll tell you my theory. That cutlery was either planted for evidence to be used against us, or – and I reckon this is more likely – it was intended as a parting gift. A sort of thank-you souvenir.'

'Souvenir?' said Tiny. 'Why would Adolf give us a souvenir?'

'Not Adolf,' said Widget. 'Somebody else, and I reckon that somebody was your actual thief.'

'So you think it wasn't cyclists nicking the stuff, it was one of his regulars?'

'Probably doing it for a laugh or 'cos he'd got a grudge against mine host.'

'Funny old world!' chuckled Joe. 'This thief, you reckon this is his way of apologising to us?'

'Quite possibly.'

'But what do we do with it? Give it back?'

'Now *you're* joking' said Tiny. 'Give it back after all we've been through and end up behind bars for our trouble? No, give it here. I'll take it into work and have it melted down and poured into a little mould. Make a little trophy. Don't know about a mermaid, but I can manage an anvil all right.'

'And what'll you do with it?'

'I shall offer it up at the next Buckshee Wheelers' dinner and when the occasion gets too riotous the pasha can bang his gavel on it to call order.'

It was generally agreed that this was a fitting end for 'Adolf's' antique cutlery. With the metal now clanking in Tiny's saddlebag, they set off, bursting spontaneously into song, Tiny conducting with his pump.

Vorder kaserne, vordern grossen tor
Stand eine laterne, und steht sie noch davor
So woll'n wirda uns wiedersch'n,
Bei der laterne
Woll'n wir stehn
Wie einst Lili Marleen,
Wie einst Lili Marleen.

It was another sort of trophy, the sad, haunting ballad of Lili Marlene that had boomed out from German radios night after night across the foxholes of the Western Desert. But now, if any stray pedestrian had glimpsed the trio flitting through the wreathing autumn mist, he might have been forgiven for imagining he had stumbled on some ghostly remnant of Rommel's Afrika Korps – the Bicycle Detachment perhaps – en route to God alone knows where and singing exultantly as only happy, drunken itinerants can.

FROM BIDLAKE TO BEIJING
VIA "THE LEAGUER"

In "A Sound of Thunder", sci-fi storywriter Ray Bradbury sends a party of time travellers on safari back to the age of the dinosaurs, with a strict warning not to step off the marked path through the prehistoric jungle. But on seeing his first Tyrannosaurus Rex, a terrified adventurer panics, loses balance and inadvertently squashes a butterfly. Returning to the present day, the men are dismayed to discover the US election has been turned on its head and a liberal president replaced by his fascist opponent.

A single event can change the course of history. You have only to imagine the woeful condition of UK cycling today if by some enormous mischance Percy Stallard, our great reformer and moderniser, had fallen to his death beneath the wheels of a Wolverhampton omnibus in 1941, and the British League of Racing Cyclists (BLRC) had never come into existence.

The Tour de France visited our shores in 2007 to a clamorous reception from the general public, media and, not least, the cycling fraternity itself. At last, it seemed, our 'Cinderella' sport was getting its just deserts. And it raised the welcome possibility that such overwhelmingly positive publicity for elite cycling might influence the motoring community to share the roads more equably with everyday pedal-pushers – the trickledown effect. For cyclists in the UK of whatever status, it was an across-the-board triumph, a mark that we now enjoyed high standing internationally after many years on the margins, and something for which we should give thanks. Mayor Livingstone, the driving force behind the bid, put the bicycle high on his Transport For London agenda, and lobbied the Tour organisers to bring the Grand Départ to London. British Cycling enthusiastically cooperated. It was a classic case of local authorities, police chiefs and government working closely together with cycle race promoters to the mutual benefit of all, something that has long been understood on the Continent, but in past times infrequently practised here. All these major players deserve great praise. But let me add another recipient for our gratitude that might surprise you. How about the British League of Racing Cyclists?

The British who? What did they have to do with it?

Sadly, some journalists and writers on cycling affairs seem to know more of European cycling history than our own, their memory default setting being 1960 with Tom Simpson and the BCF (British Cycling Federation). Typical is the following press comment:

> If [Bradley] Wiggins was called upon to appear in the latest revival of Mastermind tomorrow, his specialist subject would undoubtedly be the history of British road cycling since 1960. He is a world leader on the subject. (Brendan Gallagher, *Daily Telegraph*, 14 July 2007)

Note the cut-off point. But to be fair to Bradley, I wonder if this is strictly true? It seems likely that anyone with such a bent for history wouldn't stop at 1960 without seeking to discover how we got there. Unfortunately, in the whirlpool of journalistic comment still washing around doping and the charismatic Simpson, the far greater strategic importance of what preceded that blindingly glorious and tragic era has long been obscured and devalued. Amongst most ordinary cyclists, the civil war of 1942-58 is rarely ever mentioned, much less understood. It has been forgotten and almost erased from the record. For a few of our modern-day Basil Fawltys ('Don't mention the war!'), even rational discussion of it is anathema. Fearful of re-igniting bitter divisions by coming down on one side or the other, or else in order to avoid potential argument, the participants are lumped together in moral equivalence ('Weren't they all as bad as each other – overgrown egos in a power struggle – stubborn blockheads?'), downplaying the League's undoubted role as innovator and preserver of Continental-style road racing.

So let's be absolutely clear: prior to the National Cyclists Union (NCU) being forced by membership loss to amend its views in 1952, there was no moral equivalence. To put it in stark Manichean terms, the conflict harboured angels and demons and if the battle had been lost and the Great Satan, in the form of the unholy, obstructive alliance of the NCU and RTTC (Road Time Trials Council) had prevailed, today's cycling landscape would most likely still resemble the 1930s, with Little Britain marginalized by the big hitters of the UCI (Union

84

Cycliste Internationale). NCU policy was to retain their self-imposed ban on road racing. Even to hold massed starts on closed circuits like Brooklands, much less the open road, the die-hards had to be dragged kicking and screaming to agreement in 1933. As for engaging in any serious dialogue with 'busybodies' outside the sport – that was barred.

It was the BLRC that first legitimised our sport. They were the first to truly engage with government, the police and local authorities. Had an unreformed NCU been in power today, the golden rain of cash that has been injected into cycle sport to such great effect might have been a trickle at best. And would we ever have had roadmen of the calibre of Robinson, Simpson, Hoban, Robert and David Millar and many, many others without 'the wind beneath their wings', the incentive and basic skills acquired on the hilly nursery slopes of Britain that mimicked the Continental example?

Some might argue the BLRC was unnecessary as the NCU would have reformed itself in the fullness of time and espoused the open road. To that I would ask where would reform have come from? And when? The NCU had jogged along in its own sweet isolationist way, barring road racing for 45 years before reformist Stallard came along, and as Peter Bryant (one-time editor of *Bicycle* and co-editor of *Cycling*) said, it was quite happy to continue in this uniquely backwaters tradition:

> You can never say that if it didn't happen then this wouldn't have happened, but I can't see what else [other than the BLRC] would have brought it [massed racing on the road] about.

In any case, there was only a tiny window of opportunity for reform that opened up during World War Two when the government was otherwise engaged. Stallard seized it and by 1946 road racing was firmly established. For the Home Office to unpick this *fait accompli* would have meant resorting to time wasting legislation when the new Labour Government already had its own enormous reform agenda that took priority. Far easier, then, for it to work with, rather than oppose, the BLRC – which is what happened.

Would an unreformed NCU be at the heart of European cycling and flying high in the world, as BC is today? Would *Chef du Tour* Prudhomme have brought his Tour de France over the Channel to race (1930s style) on some closed circuit like Silverstone, or for a time trial at dawn under the aegis of an unreformed RTTC, for they also would have been under no pressure to change? Without the BLRC, would we now have any British representation in Continental road teams, any Nicole Cooke, Cavendish or Wiggins, for example? Very unlikely! That is some measure of our debt to the League.

On that day in July 2007 as I watched TV images of Millar's solo break through the wooded lanes of Kent, flickering sunlight and dappled shade created the illusion of an old black and white movie. Momentarily in my imagination there appeared a long-ago hero, a ghost at the feast. It was that difficult, tenacious, argumentative intractable man to whom we owe everything, the sturdy father figure of British road racing mounted on his vintage machine, spare tyre encircling his shoulders and the League's union jack badge pinned to his chest. We are all indebted to Stallard and his small band of brothers who together broke the bonds that, over forty-five years of dogmatic indifference, had choked the heart out of our sport and made us the laughing stock of Europe.

The Role of *The Leaguer*
To save us from this gagging anonymity and win the argument, it took the BLRC ten years and then some more. They needed to counter the opposition's propaganda machine and attract new recruits in large numbers to their 'revolutionary' agenda. Central to this role was a quarto size, sixteen-page magazine entitled *The Leaguer*.

I still recall the pleasurable anticipation I experienced as early each month a small 'Printed Paper' parcel flopped through my Sheffield council house letterbox. Oh, that whisky-breath of printer's ink! – the magazine had been rushed out to meet the deadline and was not long off the press. It was the early 1950s and I was secretary of the Falcon Road Club. We were a small organisation, never more than twenty members, picky in whom we admitted, and just one of several Sheffield clubs that observed a fanatical, almost religious devotion to The Cause. As secretary, I ordered, received and distributed copies, collected the cover price of 4d and remitted a postal order in payment. The distribution part of this took place on Friday evenings at our so-called HQ, the rented sunless backroom of a dingy city-centre pub called The Brown Cow. I recall its stale smell of sweaty pork pies and tobacco smoke. Outside, trams rattled up and down the cobbled Wicker. Inside, the lads would sit quietly digesting the magazine's contents before chatter resumed. It might be some action photo, race report, trade advertisement, the letters page or, more than likely, profile of some Continental ace that caught their eye. For aspiring *en ligne* racers like us, this monthly 'fix' of Continental-style road racing provided a focus of interest largely denied by the two commercial magazines, ultra conservative *Cycling* and somewhat more liberal *Bicycle*.

The editorial page posted news from the battlefront, the seemingly never-ending arm wrestle with the NCU and RTTC, whose joint objective was nothing less than the League's destruction and an end to road racing. Pulling at our pints of Tennant's draught and perusing *The Leaguer*, I doubt now whether any of us truly appreciated the full extent to which this was not just a battle for the League's survival, but for the heart and soul and, indeed, whole future direction of cycle sport in the UK.

We had all been raised in wartime, hand-to-mouth working class communities, where nothing was lightly cast aside and even a piece of string had value – anything less like today's throwaway society is hard to imagine. I safeguarded my copies of *The Leaguer* in a tea chest alongside my large collection of football programmes (now worth a fortune) and other memorabilia. Unfortunately, shortly before his death, my father decided to clear out the 'junk' cupboard and the whole lot went up in smoke. Since then only the odd yellowing copy of *The Leaguer* had come my way. That is until one evening when a phone call from the archivist John Scott revealed he had located a five-years'-worth treasure trove. Was I interested? You bet! I couldn't wait to connect in print with my cycling youth and, above all, rediscover how the monumental conflict had played out in the pages of a journal that told it how it was.

The Split from the Continent

At this point it would be appropriate to recall how this bitter dispute arose. Why did Britain, alone of all European nations, resort to a cycling civil war? The answer begins in the eccentricities of late 19th century England. At first, we had followed a similar path of development to other nations and our cyclists were a force to be reckoned with on the Continent. The first British winner of Bordeaux–Paris was not Tom Simpson but G. P. Mills in 1891, with compatriots Holbein second and Bates third equal. This promising course of parallel development looked set to continue until, quite out of the blue, something extraordinary happened to bring about a cataclysmic change. That 'something' (arguably one of the most important events in British cycling history) occurred on 21 July 1894 during the North Road 50-Miler. This was not even a massed start but a paced handicap race, 50 riders setting off, each with a pacer, making for a spread out field of 100. There was, of course, little motor traffic to concern them, but approaching the finish F.T. Bidlake and two other cyclists passed a horse and carriage 'idling along'. The horse reared and three cyclists fell. Bicycles were damaged, but no one was injured, and yet the lady driver complained to the local police, who, it is said, threatened to ban racing from the public highway in their locality. There was certainly no Act of Parliament nor any legislation to impede Stallard in 1942, so it follows this must have been a local affair and no more than a threat.

The pertinent question is how did this mere threat by the Huntingdonshire police assume countrywide significance three years later in 1897 when the NCU caved in and voluntarily imposed a ban on itself? What were the pros and contras? Alas we are left to guess or deduce because most NCU records kept at Coventry City library were consumed by fire during the Blitz. But there is one interesting fact: for some years after 1897 several northern clubs ignored the ban completely and raced in the old way as rebels, until isolation forced them back into line – which, to me, suggests the police threat was a bluff or confined to one county.

The Demonisation of Cyclists
Cyclists in Britain (unlike on the Continent) have never been popular with the police or the Establishment, though latter-day 'green' policies, bicycling MPs and Olympic gold medals have begun to modify this perception. Only recently has the horse-riding community seen us as allies in the struggle to reclaim country byways and calm the motorist's urge to speed. The problem in earliest days was with Penny Farthings. The noise of solid tyres rattling along the unmade roads and the sudden appearance of a rider at blinker level sometimes provoked horses to panic and bolt; hence began the demonisation of the cycling clan so well expressed by Flora Thompson in *Lark Rise to Candleford* written in the 1930s about her childhood and youth towards the end of the nineteenth century.

> But, although it was not yet realised, the revolution in transport had begun. The first high 'penny-farthing' bicycles were already on the roads and how fast these new bicycles travelled and how dangerous they looked! Pedestrians backed almost into the hedges when they met one of them, for was there not almost every week in the Sunday newspapers the story of some one being knocked down and killed by a bicycle, and letters from readers saying cyclists ought not to be allowed to use the roads, which, as everybody knew, were provided for people to walk on

or to drive on behind horses. Bicyclists ought to have roads to themselves, like railway trains was the general opinion.

From the nineteenth century to the present day, this bash-the-cyclist urge has become deeply ingrained in the British psyche. In 2003 cyclist Allan Ramsay, a Bolton driving instructor, wrote to his local paper complaining of seeing 27 motorists in short time span breaking the law whilst driving in town by using their mobile phones, one bus driver going through a red light. Far from evoking a sympathetic response, he brought down upon himself an outcry retailing the terror perpetrated by cyclists on the general population. This was the most extreme response:

All cyclists riding at night should be classed as suicide bombers. Only showing at the last minute and equally capable of inflicting death, damage and misery on anyone unfortunate enough to be near them.

Meanwhile, *The Times* had invented the term 'Lycra lout' for the aggressive urban cyclist who disregarded the rules of the road, leading calls for the green machine to be licensed and taxed. No such pejorative term exists for the vast majority of motorists who break speed limits and so endanger life; rather there is sympathy for those caught on camera and fined.

This irrational anti-cyclist campaign has backing from some very influential voices you might think should know better. Actor Nigel Havers appearing on the TV show 'Room 201' cited cyclists as one of his most hated objects to be dumped in the rubbish bin. Jeremy Clarkson ('Top Gear'), an advocate of speed at any price, has joked about running cyclists down. Best-selling novelist and newspaper columnist Tony Parsons wrote:

Cyclists are all an affront to civilised society – bicycles are for little boys doing their paper round. Bicycles are like masturbation – something you should grow out of. There is something sick and seriously stunted about grown men who want to ride a bike.

The late Ray Minovi, editor of the LVRC newsletter, suggested two reasons for 'this bizarre, irrational hatred of cyclists', neither having anything to do with riding on the pavement. One was territorial. 'You're invading our space and have no right to be on our road,' and the other envy: cyclists are free and can go pretty well anywhere you can walk.

In Flora's hierarchical society, the complaint was similar. Cyclists were intruders on the highways and byways and needed to be kept in their place. Objections from the carriage-driving elite naturally met with police approval and a blind eye was turned to individual officers who, in a spirit of boorish thuggery, stoned cyclists or put sticks in their wheels. Cab drivers also waged war, accusing them of stealing their trade. Henry Cracknell, guard of the St Albans coach, carried an iron ball on the end of a rope, which he would hurl into the wheels of passing cyclists, regardless of the consequences (at least, he was eventually brought to justice and fined). Contemporary magazines, such as *The Cyclist*, recount many such instances and the bias of magistrates, who would compound dubious charges of 'furious riding' with hefty fines out of proportion to the 'offence'.

Apart from scaring the horses, there were other reasons for the authorities to mistrust cyclists. They were blamed for introducing 'unwelcome' social change. It could be argued that female emancipation began with the bicycling 'bloomers' controversy over dress code. In 1899 Florence Warburton, a leader of the Rational Dress Movement, sued the Hautboy Hotel in Surrey for refusing to admit her to its coffee room on the grounds that her dress (knickerbockers) was unsuitable. Even though supported by the Cyclists Touring Club, she lost the case. Even more damning was the claim from members of the clergy that the bicycle promoted immorality and adultery in country areas, making it easier for illicit love affairs to flourish over greater distances than walking permitted. (In fact, later research suggests a beneficial outcome; outsiders refreshed the gene pool and diluted the pernicious effect of incest and inbreeding in remote backwaters. Ergo, more bicycling, fewer village idiots!)

There was then undoubtedly a substantial bias against cyclists, just as there is today. Yet rather than persist with the fight for their rights, the NCU chose to capitulate. Why? Our Continental neighbours had their fair share of horses and gendarmes, enough of both to involve cyclists in similar spats, yet the very idea of them being browbeaten by the Establishment is laughable. And therein lies an important difference. The French Revolution had empowered its citizens with a belief in their right to liberty, fraternity and equality, a motto inscribed in the stone pediments of buildings and enshrined in their constitution. Britain, on the other hand, deferred to the aristocracy and enshrined the class system.

Bidlake – hero or villain?

Does this explain the pusillanimity of Bidlake and co? At a time when socialism was on the rise, were they at heart conservatives with little or no belief in social equality and no stomach for the fight? As timekeeper for the Royal Aero Club and in the Schneider Trophy seaplane races during the 1930s great depression, Bidlake rubbed shoulders with wealthy conservatives. Was this why, under his influence, the NCU was persuaded to touch its forelock, roll over and defer to its 'betters'? As we shall see, Bidlake was a backwoodsman in more ways than one.

An advocate of Corinthian fair play, supposedly best exemplified in cricket (though anyone reading a biography of the ruthlessly competitive W G Grace would know this to be a sham), he idealised the 'noble' man-to-man combat of the individual time trial and was himself a record-breaking tricyclist. He hated all massed racing, even the Isle of Man race held with permission on closed roads.

Cycling magazine quoted Bidlake as calling massed racing 'a superfluous excrescence'. He continued: 'Unpaced solitary speedmen perform magnificently, unobtrusively, with no obstructive crowds and give no offence. I can't believe that our road men want to alter all this to make a Manxman's holiday.'

Of women's dress, Bidlake said:

A skirtless lady on tour is bound to suffer much. She is singularly conspicuous, a centre of observation and exposed to such contumelious ridicule as the ordinary sensitive feminine nature hesitates to provoke.

He called Rational Dress 'Laughable Dress'. And when the CTC defended Florence Warburton, Bidlake insisted that it was defending not the outfit but the CTC's contract with the hotel to serve any member of the club.

Of women's racing, he said:

Cycle racing for women is generally acknowledged to be undesirable. My ideal of a clever lady rider is one who can ride far, who can ride at a really useful speed, who mounts hills with comfort, and makes no fuss or show of effort. The stylish, clever lady stops short of being a scorcher, but if women's races were to be organised, the participants would have to run to their limit, or else make a mockery of racing. And that limit is not pleasant to contemplate ... the speed woman, dishevelled, grimy and graceless. I believe in a high standard of cycling ability as really worth while attaining by women, but not as racers. Imagine women dressed for speed, on bicycles built for speed, in attitudes necessary for speed, grabbing speed food, taking acid [strychnine dope?] and finishing dead to the world.

Take note, Nicole Cooke. And for goodness sake, in whatever we do, let us cyclists not 'give offence' on the highway, as might happen in other less civilized countries throughout the world, but let us know our place in the pecking order.

Bidlake had enormous influence in the UK for almost 40 years and even beyond (there is a memorial garden to him on the Old Great North Road, 48 miles north of London). According to Eileen Gray, C.B.E., similar patronising attitudes to women racing rumbled on in the NCU and through the early BCF*. He was hero-worshipped by cyclists until his death in 1933 (from a collision with a motor car). The Bidlake Trophy, instituted to perpetuate his memory, has been awarded annually to our outstanding racing cyclists. However, two great men, Ian Steel, winner of the Warsaw–Berlin–Prague and Brian Robinson, stage winner in the Tour de France, were both overlooked in the 1950s in deference to Bidlake's hatred of road racing, though later this seemed to have been forgotten and the trophy awarded to *en ligne* world champion racers Tom Simpson and Nicole Cooke. Poor man, he must be turning in his grave!

Could the highly articulate Bidlake, with strong conservative leanings and a hatred of massed racing, singlehandedly or with allies have swung the vote for the ban by using the police threat as his excuse?

---

* *Rebel With A Cause*, Women's Cycle Racing Association, 1999

For whatever the reason, the 1897 split with Europe is now recognised as an unmitigated disaster. Whereas Continental cycling established close ties with community and government as a result of the growing popularity and commercialisation of road racing, in particular the Tour de France, Britain took the opposite path. By banning road racing and shunning local contact with extra-sportive authority, it locked itself for 45 years into a voluntary form of apartheid, the disastrous policy of 'Cycling for Cyclists'. Even today this fact is not widely understood. Asked on Radio 4's 'Today' programme why time trialing predominated in Britain, time trialist Michael Hutchinson (author of *The Hour*) put it down to a police ban. Sorry, Michael, but this was a convenient half-truth bandied around by the RTTC to defend the indefensible. What evidence we have points to a voluntary self-imposed ban enthusiastically promoted by the Bidlake-ites.

Stallard and the opposition

This potted history gives some idea of what Stallard had to face in 1942 when he restarted road racing in the teeth of virulent opposition. The NCU and RTTC were suffering from a form of institutional paranoia that defied rational argument. In their minds the authorities, given the chance, were still out to get them. Trying to enlighten these boneheads was like trying to kick a plastic football through a brick wall. He had to deal with prejudiced, irrational people, like NCU secretary A. P. Chamberlin, people with closed minds, terrified of change, and people like NCU/RTTC bigwig Alex Josey:

> At the moment the Government is too busily occupied to do much about it, but action must come sooner or later. I was personally concerned at the beginning of the war with this unfortunate rebel movement and I tried hard to crush it in the interests of cyclists generally.*

Goodness knows, Stallard argued his case and took no hasty action, but ultimately he failed. The only course left open to him was to demonstrate their folly in a practical way by promoting

---

* Presumably this preceded the 1942 split at a time when Stallard and company were arguing their case within the NCU and as NCU members.

the 1942 Llangollen–Wolverhampton road race, the first on British soil for almost half a century, with the support of both police and local authority. Even this 'proof' didn't convince his opponents. As a consequence, he and his supporters were at first suspended then banned by the NCU/RTTC axis (according to John Dennis of the Catford CC, because war service had reduced club membership to a rump, the officials concerned were in effect one and the same people) and the only way forward for them was to form their own organisation, the BLRC.

Radical opposition to the new body came from *Cycling's* (now *Cycling Weekly*) Harry H England, the editor, and its chief columnist and opinion-former George Herbert Stancer ('GHS').

If we voluntarily place road racing under police control we sign its death warrant. It will need only a few serious accidents, a few complaints from influential motorists, a few protests from big-wigs and busybodies, to bring an instruction from the Home Office that all road racing must be stopped.
George H Stancer, *Cycling*, 8 July 1942)

Two things emerge. Firstly, the nationwide ban of 1897 had been voluntary – if a legal ban had been in force, then the police could have acted upon it immediately without needing 'an instruction from the Home Office'. Some cyclists still allege, wrongly, that the BLRC acted in defiance of the law. There was no such law. Secondly, Stancer and his allies were so institutionally paranoid that it never seemed to occur to them that as there was a war on, petrol was rationed and Britain's roads all but devoid of traffic. The government had other far more important problems than the BLRC to concern themselves with.

Former Racing Editor of *The Bicycle*, John Dennis, who believes the NCU have been unfairly vilified, argues:

It was understandable that there was a fear that cycle racing on open roads could be banned quite easily for military and security reasons, thereby robbing cycling's dedication to road time trials.

He adds that Stallard's race took place in the Midlands, far removed from trigger points in London and on the south coast, making it more acceptable to the authorities. Nevertheless, he asserts that it represented a dangerous gamble with the RTTC's future.

This might have been the case in 1942-44 when, in the run-up to D-Day, there was increased military activity on road and rail. But by 1945, road racing had indeed spread south to the Home Counties unchallenged by the police or local authorities (viz below, the three-day Southern Grand Prix held in August 1944 in Kent's Buzz-Bomb Alley). Had 'military and security reasons' really existed, this particular stage race, in a particularly dangerous area, just after D-Day would have been immediately banned by the authorities, instead of being accepted as a morale-boosting example of how we plucky Brits were cocking a snook at Hitler and, despite the continuous threat of air raids, conducting 'business as usual' (the defiant sign posted in shop windows after bombing raids). And how does John explain why NCU opposition continued long after the war ended and right up to 1952? Again, as in 1897, it seems the threat was being exaggerated by the Bidlake-ites, and the spineless NCU allowed itself to be led by the nose, John's Catford CC being a noble exception.

In fact, Stallard, with his sense for politics and bold Churchillian instinct, struck at the moment in history that offered him the best chance of success, probably the only chance. Going cap in hand to the Home Office post-1960, when traffic was increasing exponentially, would have met with a sharp rebuff. The BLRC succeeded in getting road racing permission cemented into law around 1960 only because they presented the Home Office with a *fait accompli*, together with proof that it was not a dangerous sport as its opponents had alleged (In fact, recent statistics show that racing in a bunch is far less lethal than time trialing – visibility being a key factor).

Moreover, to suggest the government would have imposed a blanket ban to include time trialing, a sport conducted in secret at dawn on empty roads, that disavowed spectators and gave no offence to anyone (according to Josey), strikes me as utterly absurd. How would such a ban have been enforced? By local constables rising early on the off chance of spotting a bicycle race, whilst employing every police car in the county to pursue every lone cyclist and clock them for furious riding? (No printed numbers were used; riders identified themselves by shouting their numbers to the timekeeper.) One can imagine how delighted the magistrates would be to have their courts clogged up with such piffling 'offences'.

And all this at 6 a.m. on a Sunday morning? Who did these stuffy RTTC officials imagine they were dealing with? MI5? They must have had a very exaggerated idea of their own importance in the socio-political life of Britain.

The Bicycle, to its credit, gave Stallard a fair hearing. But *Cycling*, the oldest, biggest and most influential magazine, with all the authority of tradition weighting its opinion, for the next nine years supported the NCU and refused outright to publish anything but anti-BLRC propaganda – no, not even its race results. What eventually changed its mind was the cycle trade's thumbs up to the 1951 *Daily Express* Tour of Britain. In the end, money spoke loud and *Cycling* conceded, not daring to snub its advertisers.

But long before this, the fathers of the League had realised they must counter this torrent of abuse and calumny with their own organ of propaganda. As it was, survival was touch and go. The NCU/RTTC had the established club structure in an arm lock. Where were converts to The Cause to come from? How many cyclists would stick their heads over the parapet and break the habits and friendships of a lifetime to join a rebel body whose chances of failure were high? The answer is not many at first. But again the opposition had reckoned without the effects of the war. Many clubmen recruited into the armed services were stationed overseas and, freed of close ties with club life, could think more independently (like the Buckshee Wheelers). Change was in the air. Labour's shock landslide victory over Churchill's Conservatives in the 1945 General Election was spurred on by the radicalisation our armed forces underwent at the hands of leftward-leaning education officers, our Soviet ally being cited as the ideal of social equality. After the sacrifices of war, the troops demanded a better life for themselves and their families, blaming fuddy-duddy conservatism for previous failures to deliver a programme of social advancement. What could be more fuddy-duddy, complacent and stick-in-the-mud than the NCU and RTTC? In that heady atmosphere of the New Jerusalem, the BLRC found its niche as the one progressive and innovative body prepared to take cycling forward to the sunny uplands. Not immediately in 1942, or even 1946 as the troops came home and caution still prevailed, but within ten years the drip of new recruits would become a surge.

The Leaguer is launched

So it was in June 1949, when BLRC membership hovered at around

1,000 as against 60,000 for the NCU/RTTC, *The Leaguer* came into being. As a monthly magazine with one name change to *The Racing Cyclist* in the mid 1950s, it endured for a decade until becoming redundant when the two bodies merged into the BCF. At first it struggled. Two predecessors – *Cycling Record* and *Cyclo Sport* – had both failed. A similar fate for *The Leaguer* would have delivered a devastating psychological blow to the BLRC and its self-crafted image as a dynamic organisation that meant what it said and got things done. For two years it teetered on the edge and at one point, when still heavily subsidised and losing £20 (about £1000 in today's money) per month, was saved from bankruptcy and closure only by a narrow vote of the NEC to inject more funds.

We have grown used to living in our so-called age of 'Affluenza', the virus-like doctrine that the continuous accumulation of wealth and its trappings is a desirable end in itself. Sport cries out for subsidy from the public or private purse as the price of success, and some of its stars have become as wealthy as Croesus. The BLRC was from a different age. Cash starved yet rich in ideals and ambition, it performed on a steam head of passion for reform. And yet, despite its paucity of funding, lacking even a proper headquarters, its enormous achievements must rank pound for pound as a proud model for the economic efficiency behind BC's recent success. As far as one can tell, all its officials occupied honorary posts and received nothing but expenses for their Herculean efforts (Jimmy Kain even subsidised the Brighton–Glasgow stage race from his own pocket). The magazine was no exception. The first editor was A. H. Groves, assisted by a circulation manager, A. Bailey, both of Nottingham. Later an advertising manager was appointed. The editor had to ensure a sufficient supply of material each month to fill 16 quarto-size pages. Anyone involved in magazine production will know what this meant in practice: writing editorials, seeking contributors and editing copy, persuading race organisers to submit reports and results on time, striving to widen the advertising base, putting the whole thing to bed at the printers on the due date – and doing all this single-handedly, not just once but for month after month. Groves achieved this in his spare time when also, incidentally, he acted as BLRC vice-chairman.

The magazine's cover price was originally 4d, but as it expanded in size this increased to 6d (the café price of a pot of tea) and by 1958, as *The Racing Cyclist*, 9d. Distribution was via club secretaries or vendors to the crowds assembled at race venues. Some lightweight cycle dealers sold copies off the counter on a sale-or-return basis. When, however, an approach was made to wholesale newspaper distributors for the magazine to be represented nationwide on newsagents' shelves, this request was denied, allegedly due to coercion from the powerful Hulton Press, Cycling's publishers.

Given *The Leaguer*'s parlous financial state it is little wonder that gloomy appeals to the membership became a recurrent theme. March 1951 saw the editor thundering like Corporal Frazer in 'Dad's Army':

This Mag is Doomed: the circulation rate has not increased sufficiently. You have just read the appeals, sat back and done nothing about it. The remedy is in your hands. Yes, I mean YOU.

Such hectoring would today be anathema. Then, however, young national servicemen, accustomed to parade ground discipline, instinctively jumped to attention. Successful or not, such strident appeals became redundant as within six months the Tour of Britain brought road racing to the front pages of a national daily newspaper and advertising revenues rolled in from the big boys of the trade. Hitherto volume manufacturers such as BSA, Wearwell and Hercules had fought shy of *The Leaguer*. But now this important mass-marketing sales opportunity inspired their gratitude. Of course they knew their own off-the-peg assembly-line bikes would never set your typical Continent-obsessed Leaguer roadman alight, nonetheless it seemed wise to throw a handful of corn to the goose that had laid the golden egg. After all, advertising in a magazine with few overheads and no salary bill was as cheap as chips. A full-length quarter page ad was a snip at three pounds five shillings for six months. Thus, from near bankruptcy, 'the Mag' quickly rose to a profit of £10 per month and the funding crisis was over.

NCU Outmanoeuvred
A charge often levelled at the BLRC was of wild irresponsibility (again see Josey's comments). Stallard and his colleagues were characterised as selfish, immature hotheads who gave little thought to the consequences of their actions. GHS accused them of 'seizing ownership of Britain's roads' and thus risking a backlash from the political elite. What would happen, he wanted to know, if racing

motorists demanded their 'right' to promote a British-style Mille Miglia on the public highway? The government would be forced to legislate and its wrath would fall indiscriminately upon the heads of all cyclists, including the blameless RTTC. But yet again the League wrong-footed its critics by courting the very VIPs it was supposed to be inflaming, the prime example being the famous 'Loyal Address' to King George V1. This was a masterstroke of publicity devised by secretary Jimmy Kain on the occasion of the 1945 'Victory Race' from Brighton to Glasgow. Kain hit on the idea of presenting a scroll to the King at Buckingham Palace following the London stage. It was headed:

TO THE KING'S MOST EXCELLENT MAJESTY

Loyal and dutiful address of the British League of Racing Cyclists by its Chairman and Committee, Honorary Secretaries and Members:

Most Gracious Sovereign –

Nowadays this unctuous, fawning script replete with curlicues seems like something out of a Gilbert and Sullivan comic opera, but in that age of deference to the Royals, it was not at all extraordinary, the Loyal Toast being always top of the agenda at club dinners and the national anthem played in theatres and cinemas. From it unfolds a skilful argument to evoke the king's sympathy and support. First, the King and his ministers are congratulated for 'the victory by your Majesty's forces over your Majesty's enemies in Europe.' Then attention is drawn to the part played in this great achievement by 'the Youth of your Majesty's Realm', enhanced by their physical fitness 'due to their indulgence in the many sports for which your Majesty's subjects are universally renowned.'

Then the link is made with cycle racing. 'It is humbly submitted that among these sports, cycling occupied a worthy place.'

The piece contains Churchillian phraseology such as 'the darkest days of war' that Kain must have known would be music to the King's ears. The address ends in an expression of hope that 'all sports, including the sport of Cycling, may be resumed and long continued in Peace, so that the objects of our League, namely, the development of healthy competition and friendly rivalry in Cycling Events may proceed unhampered.'

The response from Buckingham Palace was immediate:

The King will be grateful if you will convey to the members of the League his sincere thanks for this Address, the terms of which he much appreciates.

The extent to which the Address was really tongue-in-cheek may be arguable but not the skill of the writer or the timing. All through the war the Royals had been desperate to play down their German origins and privileged background. Remaining in London throughout the Blitz was part of their policy to appear less remote and identify themselves with the suffering of the common people. Jimmy Kain had hit the button, for what could be more plebeian than the humble bicycle that millions of factory workers employed to get them to work?

What a coup! It amounted to a royal stamp of approval for the League's road racing policy. Note how Kain slipped in that plea '…friendly rivalry in Cycling Events may proceed unhampered.' Who was doing the 'hampering' if not Stancer, and NCU and RTTC officials? How they must have spluttered over the news that a major plank of their opposition had been cut from under their feet. Now a complaining chief constable might be silenced with the words, 'Well, His Majesty approves, so what's your problem?'

Signing up the Bigwigs

This event preceded the publication of *The Leaguer* but was by no means an isolated example of the politically astute BLRC's way of winning influential people to its cause. Each such success was reported in the magazine with brio: here, for example, an account from July 1952 of the League's 10th Anniversary Celebration Dinner at the Tatton Sykes Hotel, Wolverhampton. In attendance were many of the Llangollen–Wolverhampton riders from 1942, the victorious 1952 Warsaw–Berlin–Prague team led by Ian Steel, BLRC national officials and, of course, the press – but more importantly, from the top drawer of respectable society, the Lord Mayor, Assistant Chief Constable and two local members of parliament.

The Mayor, a cycling enthusiast, toasting Percy as guest of honour, commended him for his dogged determination to put road racing on the map, and christened him 'Persevering Percy!'

Mr Gillott, *Express and Star*, said, amid great laughter, that he had received a *semi-threatening letter from the NCU* [my italics] for sponsoring the event. The two MPs, the Assistant Chief Constable and Mr Swallow, Managing Director of the *Express and Star*, all gave excellent and humorous speeches, and all showed that they know more than a little about the League and its activities, which is what we have come to expect in the seat of the League's birthplace.

By courting press publicity (and, incidentally, wrong-footing its opponents) the BLRC hoped to go beyond organising a programme of racing for the membership, crucial as this was. The overriding aim was much more ambitious: to bring the sport to the attention of the whole British public; to lift road racing's profile far above mere toleration to the zenith of popular affection it enjoyed on the Continent. This was then not inconceivable. Before the advent of mass car ownership the bicycle was a major means of transport to and from work (16% of all such trips, more than by car) and it was easy for people to identify with the courage, skill, determination and sheer effort required to ride an upgraded version of their own humble push-bikes over great distances at high speed. Before television brought sporting images into every living room, the bicycle race, starting and finishing in the suburbs of a major town or city, made for an exciting and colourful spectacle that enticed spectators out onto the streets. The BLRC sought to bring cycling to the people, not hide it away from them in some shameful dark corner. To lend weight to their cause, they courted influential public figures and furnished them with photo opportunities: dropping a start flag (the Butlin's 7-Days was flagged off by a Chief Inspector Farrow), presenting the prizes or, as in this case, attending a celebration dinner. Photos of Lord Mayors, chief constables, business managers, MPs, beauty queens, stars of stage, screen and radio all figure in *The Leaguer* – all shamelessly recruited to lend respectability to a sport that under the previous regime had not dared utter its name. Where the powerful went, the press followed, grinding more publicity for the BLRC. In the case of a road race promising a celebrity appearance, large crowds would assemble, alerted beforehand to the proceedings by an article in the local paper, leafleting of pubs and shops, and a loudspeaker hailer touring the area on top of a vehicle. The power of such publicity is illustrated by the enormous crowds lining the route of the *Daily Express* Tour of Britain, not far short of those in South East England for the 2007 Tour.

Local representation was important, as in Wolverhampton, but so too were allies at national and parliamentary level in order to rebut opposition from whatever quarter it might come. *The Leaguer* reported in January 1952 that Lord Donegal had agreed to become BLRC president. Between September and December a veritable deluge of bigwigs accepted vice-presidencies: Lord Douglas of Kirtleside KCB MC DFC, chairman of BEA; Brigadier Flavell, Lord Baden Powell of scouting fame and baronet Sir Harold Bowden of Sturmey Archer gears, himself a prolific cyclist as well as owning a firm 'which produces over a million machines a year!'

The Leaguer comments:

Sir Harold has been through every stage of bicycle making from the bench up. In 1901 his father bought the patents for the Sturmey-Archer 3-speed gear. Sir Harold and a friend were sent to test the gear against 20 professional riders in severe hill climbing trials between Grenoble and Chambery. He has travelled far and wide; on one occasion he sold twelve ladies' machines to an agent in Gibralter. They were for the Sultan of Morocco, who liked to relax and watch the ladies of the harem riding round in diaphanous costumes!

An entire harem cycling in see-through dresses – surely a sex toy beyond even the wit of Ann Summers!

Hard Men, Hard Times

A cycling baronet, a Sultan and his harem, a British cycle manufacturer turning out a million bikes a year – the pages of *The Leaguer* return us to an era somewhere over the rainbow in what for today's youngsters must seem like a never-never land. To 21st century sensibilities some of the detail can be alien in its naivety. Humour, for example, is unashamedly Goonish. Dr I Killem-Quick (The Eminent Crackpotologist) posts a series of fitness and training articles that would not have gone amiss in *The Dandy*. Political correctness has no voice and there is a wistful innocence about club dinners being described as 'gay evenings', women as 'the gentle sex' and occasional references to 'ten little nigger boys' or 'a nigger in the woodpile'. A brief paragraph in June 1951 casually records that all the girl members of top Polhill RC have been expelled. Why, for goodness sake? Were they getting in the way of serious training, their seductive charms too much of a distraction for the racing boys to bear? We are not told. Blatant misogyny that would nowadays provoke outrage in the press passes without comment, much less protest.

Then there is a debate in the letters page started by former Brighton–Glasgow winner George Kessock questioning the growing tendency for longer and longer races and pointing out that, whilst the professional Tour de France averages only (only!) 130 miles per stage, the amateur/independent Tour of Britain has stages of 140 and 160, and the 1000-mile Butlin's 7-Days averages over 140. Support from fellow independent Len Hook (A5 Road Club) claims negative racing as a consequence. Two issues later and fitness correspondent and soon-to-be-editor Charles Fearnley warns: 'riding too long too young is not a good idea.' But nothing changes. The debate seems to go on for years. In October 1953 Sheffield correspondent Roy Bramhall is still arguing the same case, that the average TOB stage (135 miles) is far too long. Still nothing changes. The eight-day 1954 Amateur Circuit of Britain (ACB) covers 1000 miles, or 125 per day, with a final stage from Wolverhampton to London (won by Tynesider Don Sanderson) of 150. In case you miss the point: this was a race for amateurs, taking in *en route* the mountains of the Pennines, Lakeland and Wales.

The fact is that a powerful faction of the BLRC belonged in spirit to the SAS Tendency, none more so than Vic Humphrey, ACB organiser. He sought out stages of extraordinary length and toughness, including the hazard of unmade mountain tracks with sprouting grass and cattle-grids, a devil to climb and a nightmare to descend. The ACB, sponsored by Quaker Oats, ran for three years 1954-6, each race tougher than the last. To the credit of participants, despite conditions sometimes resembling an early Tour de France, only once did the overall average speed fall fractionally below 20mph. Humphrey's thinking (with strong backing from the League's shakers and movers) was the longer and tougher a race the better (the 160 miles Tour of the Chilterns was another of his classic promotions). If we ever fielded a team in the Tour, it was argued, it might lack for speed but certainly not stamina.

That those early League 'boys' were hard men, both as riders and organisers, is not in question. They had survived the 1930s

Great Depression, World War II and the ensuing regimentation and deprivations of National Service. Nourishment for the athlete in the face of Austerity Britain food rationing was not infrequently discussed in *The Leaguer*. How to choose the right food was topical – but in all my reading I never once came across the word 'obesity'. Rationing enabled people to keep the input of calories more easily in balance with the output in terms of exercise.

The Amateur Circuit of Britain (the 'Oats') in the Welsh mountains, 1954

Something of that bold, make do and endure spirit comes through in a graphic article, 'Speaking of Tours', by Manchester independent Les Plume, 'winner of the first stage race ever held in Britain'. It appears in the November 1952 issue:

The Tour of Britain is now established and the dreams of the League's early pioneers have been fulfilled. But how many people realise that the foundations of the Tour were laid in the first week of August 1944? After weeks of work by Wally Summers and Jimmy Kain, the first multi-stage race ever organised in Britain, the three-day Southern Grand Prix, was held in the county of Kent, nicknamed at that period 'Buzz Bomb Alley'.

Not only had the League to contend with bitter opposition from the cycling press, but also with the many Flying Bombs that came over in the course of the three-days' racing. At that time it seemed as though even Adolf Hitler had joined forces with the opposition!

As I followed this year's mighty (1952) Tour through the counties of England into Wales and Scotland, together with its attendant caravan of official cars, motorcyclists, newsreel press and BBC announcers, the Southern GP of 1944 did indeed seem a very insignificant beginning.

When the Manchester team arrived in wartime London we were greeted by a pretty grim picture. Rubble and bomb damage seemed everywhere. Several of the streets near Lewisham Town Hall were blocked, a Flying Bomb having fallen a couple of hours previously. So the official start was moved five miles further on to the Fantails Restaurant.

A big marquee had been erected and straw paliasses were issued to all riders and officials. This was to be HQ and sleeping quarters for the next three days.

The course consisted of an outward run of 15 miles to a 12 miles circuit, then a varying number of laps on the circuit according to the length of the stage. Finally, the 15 miles run in to the finish. There were three climbs on the course: River Hill, Polhill and Quarry Hill. Over the three days the field climbed these twenty times.

The race started at 5.30 on Saturday evening, and I remember the sigh of relief from timekeeper Jimmy Kain when the Wolverhampton contingent, including Percy Stallard and Ralph Jones, arrived, as non-starters were numerous.

Prior to the start we received a lecture on stage racing. Several pre-war Tour de France magazines were pinned on a big blackboard for our benefit. Yes, it was just like school! But we were all willing pupils.

As we lined up, the sirens wailed an alarm and it was a very small band of people who witnessed the start of Britain's first stage race. The starter was the late Victor Berlemont. (ed. Berlemont was a Poirot-moustachioed character from London's Soho. He kept The French House in Dean Street, a pub famed for its association with General de Gaulle and the Resistance, and as a drinking hole later frequented by louche writers and artists such as Dylan Thomas and Francis Bacon. It was the nearest thing to Parisian life you could find at that time in Britain.)

The pace for the first stage was quite fast, and as we swept down River Hill I saw my first Flying Bomb sailing along just above the peloton, sounding something like a two-stroke motorcycle. I was undecided whether to dive into the nearest ditch, but to the London boys it was just another doodlebug, and they were far too busy trying to break away to worry about such trifles.

A 'Flying Bomb sailing along just above the peloton' – that still carries resonance today. You can imagine its put-putting motor cutting out and the bomb beginning its downward plunge as the racers dived into the ditch. Les comments that the crowd assembled at the finish had only just emerged from bomb shelters on hearing the all-clear siren.

Winning a prime in the 'Oats', 1954

Soaked to the skin but happy – 'Oats' stage-winner Rhyl, 1954

The Dirty Tricks Brigade

If those early League boys were hard men, the BLRC negotiators had to be somewhat more compromising if in the early 50s they hoped to do a deal with what Les calls the opposition. For deal it had to be, and only Stallard and a few other diehards argued for a fight to the finish. The League's negotiating stance was, by and large, conciliatory. On the other side, the NCU/RTTC became increasingly belligerent and shifty. Their tactic was to procrastinate in the hope that, long-term, something might happen to drive the League out of business. It has to be said, in face of Home Office threats to legislate, their procrastination gambled more dangerously with cycling's future than Stallard ever did. The BLRC's friends in Parliament and the House of Lords played an important role in holding this catastrophe at bay, whilst for its part the treacherous RTTC probably made representations behind the scenes to the Home Office to have the BLRC banned, sometimes in desperation resorting to downright lying. In January 1952, presumably under threat of court action, the RTTC was obliged to issue an apology for an untruth that had appeared in its June Bulletin prior to the first Tour of Britain:

Mr W.C. Rains, the Honorary General Secretary of the British League of Racing Cyclists, Mr D Peakall, their Honorary stage Events Coordinator and Mr A H Groves, their Vice-Chairman, have complained of the publication in the June 'Bulletin' on the Council's statement on the menace of massed-start racing on the Highways (Reason 4), that 'The motive behind the majority of ringleaders and their associates is financial; the possibility of extracting sums of money from unsuspecting concerns or newspapers (to whom a distorted story has been told) and the further possibility that unsuspecting newspapers would give valuable free advertisement to trade interests bound up with the promotions.'

We are now informed that this statement is inaccurate and that in fact the newspapers and commercial concerns who sponsor those events are most anxious to do so and pay a sum only sufficient to provide the expenses of the event and the prizes to competitors. Neither the organisers nor their officials responsible for the promotion receive any financial benefit whatsoever and certainly no distorted stories are told to the sponsors.

We desire unreservedly to withdraw the statements quoted above, which we realise should not have been made and we tender to Mr Rains, Mr Peakall and Mr Groves our sincere apologies for having made and published them.

R. MacQueen, Editor

In the run-up to the first TOB, the League's top negotiators had been accused of being on the make and take. How shameful that the mealy mouthed RTTC had to be forced into this grovelling apology by the threat of libel action and ruinous damages that could have bankrupted its officials and put the organisation itself out of business. It says much for the BLRC that it accepted the apology with good grace rather than pursue a fellow cycling organisation down the path of litigation.

The Leaguer's role was to counter the incessant anti-BLRC propaganda and misrepresentation of the facts, which appeared in the Bulletin and pages of *Cycling* (An appeal to editor England in June 1951 to lessen his bias fell on deaf ears as he railed against the forthcoming Tour of Britain and refused to publish a letter of reply). To its credit, *The Leaguer* strove to be open and honest with its readership, never disguising the difficulty of the task nor exaggerating its successes. But the negotiating trail proved to be long and winding and to do its ins and outs full justice would require a whole book. Here, then, are just a few of the highs and lows in that sixteen years' epic journey as portrayed in 'the mag'.

First, to be absolutely clear: the BLRC never sought to take over or bully its rivals. It sought accommodation and its stance was defensive. It was quite content for the NCU to control track racing and the RTTC time trialing as long as it in return controlled road racing, a right it felt it had earned.

At first, after 1942 the NCU and RTTC simply refused point blank to negotiate for fear of thus giving legitimacy to 'the outlaws'. (Governments always say: 'We do not negotiate with terrorists,' though they usually end up by doing just that). But by late 1951 the NCU was forced to change its tune. It was losing members, and sometimes even entire clubs, to a BLRC high on prestige from the Tour of Britain. It could hardly continue ignoring an organisation with support in the House of Lords and so it reluctantly agreed to open a dialogue. The problem came, as ever, from the RTTC with whom the NCU seemed irretrievably entwined in a stultifying *pas de deux*. Reconciliation? The RTTC would have none of it.

National Unity – Hopes of 'healing the split' have received a further set-back as a result of the latest RTTC dictum. We were outlawed because our type of racing was 'dangerous' and 'agin the law'. Since these two fallacies have been exploded, the hierarchy of the time trial world has turned to sheer slanging tactics.

 The NCU–BLRC meeting decided on a further meeting, with the hopes of RTTC representation, but these now appear to be shattered. The cycling world is even more split than before, with the League and the RTTC at extremes and the Union sitting gingerly on the fence. Which way will they leap?
(*The Leaguer*, August 1951)

Flip-flop
Which way? The answer came in May 1952 when, by secret agreement with the RTTC, the NCU leapt in a direction that took the whole cycling world by surprise. For ten years it had denounced road racing as dangerous and arrant folly; now suddenly it flip-flopped

and declared it would commence its own road racing programme in June, unashamedly inviting BLRC members to acquire legitimacy by affiliating to its ranks. So what had happened to produce this unexpected conversion? Had NCU officials been struck by a bolt of lightning on the road to Damascus and made to realise the error of their ways? Were they now convinced at long last of the paramount importance of road racing? No, the truth was very different. NCU membership was in sharp decline and most of their star riders had taken out independent licences with trade teams competing in the Tour of Britain. The civil war had alerted the UCI to the fact that the Union was out of step and pressure for reform was also coming from that quarter. It was becoming plain to the Union that it had no alternative but to vomit up ten years of spleen and undergo a course of detoxification.

But there was to be no apology for the half-century of wasted opportunity, nor any hand of friendship extended. Far from that, they simply stole the BLRC's racing rulebook word for word. Even more unbelievably, this Sleeping Giant now rudely awakened, that had never organised a single road race in its whole existence, had the preposterous cheek to approach the *Daily Express* with a proposal to run the 1953 Tour of Britain! Needless to say, with its inexperience and previous incompetence unmasked, the NCU met with a sharp rebuff.

In fact, over the following years, due to lack of will and expertise, very few NCU road races were promoted. And the conversion had come too late for those many former NCU members, with a genuine interest in road racing, who had already quit and joined the BLRC. Whilst this NCU about-turn did no immediate damage to the League, it enormously complicated cycling's relationship with the MOT, now alarmed at the prospect of road race numbers suddenly doubling. The fear of ensuing chaos brought increasing pressure from government for the two bodies to unify and it was this above all that led to the eventual formation of the BCF in a shotgun wedding.

Break through
As for the UCI, it had long accepted that the BLRC was the best body to control road racing. And the politically adroit League had been busy courting powerful support on the Continent just as it had done in Britain. Amongst its strongest supporters was the influential sporting

magazine *L'Equipe*. The UCI would have loved to recognise the BLRC without further ado and ditch the stick-in-the-mud NCU. But how could it ditch a relationship of seventy years without being accused of disloyalty and the possibility of being challenged in court? Instead it sought compromise. At the 1953 Paris Conference a proposition was put to allow the BLRC one year's temporary affiliation. The NCU delegation was so outraged that it walked out of the meeting before the vote. How stupid! The proposition was passed by the narrowest of margins and would have failed had the British delegation remained in the room.

Now *The Leaguer* could rejoice in what it saw as the first step towards full international recognition:

IN – AT LAST!

To say that the League is jubilant at gaining UCI recognition would be to put it mildly, but it has not gone to our heads and we are still trying, as we have done for years, to get an honourable agreement with the other two cycling bodies.

Moving rapidly to seize the initiative, the BLRC Management and Negotiating Committees met and issued a statement:

Bearing in mind the MOT edict that the road racing programmes be unified, the BLRC is prepared to accept the responsibility of the control of road racing. NCU clubs who propose to promote road races will be encouraged to affiliate. The BLRC feel that permanent unity can be achieved by a tripartite agreement between the specialist organisations in this country.

To ensure unified representation to the International body, it is recommended that a small controlling Bureau be created by equal representation from the three organisations concerned. It is known that this will meet with the approval of the UCI officials.

'Honourable agreement.' The tone is not triumphant, but moderate and reasonable, an olive branch extended to its rivals: 'Let's get our heads together and sort this out.' At this point in 1953 cyclists of whatever persuasion had good reason to believe agreement was just around the corner. But they were to be sadly disappointed. The NCU/RTTC axis had other ideas.

When the three bodies met to thrash out the agreement, it was the BLRC that made all the concessions. It allowed the NCU to continue promoting up to 250 road races a year, whilst at the same time giving up its own right to promote track races and time trials. Yet for all that it failed to budge the NCU on the matter of a single International Racing Licence, meaning BLRC riders would still have to affiliate to the Union in order to race abroad. This 'give-away agreement' nearly split asunder the BLRC, some sections being in favour of peace at any price for the sake of unity, others claiming the League had been betrayed. Once again both sides of the argument found a democratic voice in *The Leaguer*.

Percy puts his foot down

February 1954 saw Percy Stallard vociferous in his condemnation. In a closely argued article, 'What of the Future?' he unpicked the main tenets of the agreement and urged the BLRC not to ratify it. It had been folly, he said, to recognise the NCU's right to promote road races, especially in terms 'that threatened to destroy the Independent class, which had done so much to build up the reputation of the League and had made shamamateurism an unnecessary evil.' (Shamateurism prevailed in the NCU and RTTC).

Peter Bryan, one time editor of *The Bicycle*, later managing editor of *Cycling* said of Stallard:

> He was a bright and energetic man but he had the most abrasive nature that I have ever met. He could never believe that he could have a bad idea or make a bad decision. And sometimes he'd go berserk with those who disagreed with him. He didn't have, let us say, the delicacies of negotiation.

It has also been said of him that having achieved what he wanted, with the NCU's final acceptance of massed racing on the road, he placed the continuity of the BLRC over the end of the civil war. He apparently said: 'The NCU were running road races and we were running road races and there wasn't any need for amalgamation of the NCU and the BLRC, to form the BCF at all.'

To my mind these criticism fail to stand up to rational scrutiny. To cite an 'abrasive nature' as a fault is to put political dealing over principle. Stallard felt that unification had nothing to offer but a compromise that would destroy the high ideals and aims he had set for the BLRC. With hindsight, can anyone say he was wrong? Or that the BCF from its inception until its quasi-collapse in 1996, with a whiff of corruption over the Doyle affair, had been a better organisation than the BLRC? Leaders are expected to lead and in the process, like Churchill and Roosevelt, for good or ill, become single-minded. So be it. If Stallard can be accused of anything, it is that he refused to acknowledge the threat from the Home Office. He probably believed it was like the threat of the Huntingdonshire police in 1894 and the presupposed 'threat' of 1942, not to be taken seriously.

Stallard, who did not mince his words, may have been on occasion a ranter, lacking the subtle two-handed sophistry that one can acquire through the process of higher education. He did not go out of his way to compromise with, in his view, half-blind idiots. Yet, as shown by the following extract, he could when necessary be a lucid and formidable opponent in written debate.

> If this agreement is ever accepted by the BLRC, it will have lost its fight on behalf of British Road Sport, and it will be only a matter of time before the League is forced out of existence by the conniving of the other two bodies. The UCI recognition, which we now enjoy, would be lost immediately the NCU reported to the UCI congress that the BLRC accepted them as the recognised body (for road racing).
>
> Our first efforts must be directed towards assuring that we retain our UCI recognition and persuading the UCI to stop the NCU encroaching upon our preserves; after all, road racing has been matured by the BLRC without any outside support and against all attempts by the NCU to destroy it. It was only when the failure of these attempts had been made apparent by a considerable loss in membership that the NCU decided to try and rob the BLRC of its birthright by promoting road races in opposition.

Clearly, Percy feared his baby would go down the plughole with the bath water. Besides the tri-partite agreement, he touched on other topics to do with the BLRC's organisation. Never drawn to laissez-faire, he sought always to drive standards up. He proposed proportional representation on decision-making bodies, each region being allocated votes according to the size of its membership (like the present-day European Union). He demanded that promoters of professional or Independent races should in future require 'certain qualifications' and the approval of the NEC before being allowed to go ahead under BLRC rules – there being too many sloppy 'cowboy' promotions bringing discredit to the organisation. He had strong views on the selection of International teams based on his own considerable experience as a team manager:

> To my knowledge the most successful teams are not composed entirely of riders who have a long list of wins to their credit. The inclusion of a certain number of domestiques is a vital necessity.

Professional teams are now routinely organised on this basis. He also drew attention to the continuing need 'to devise means of giving publicity to our cause', and bemoaned the fact that 'whilst we are accepting an increased number of invitations to compete abroad I think I am right in saying that not one foreign amateur competed in BLRC events last year, and this, to me, as one particularly interested in international racing, is a deplorable state of affairs.'

Above all, Percy was a great visionary. This is what he had to say about the then rigid division of sport into professionals and amateurs.

> I look forward to the inevitable day when the barriers which separate amateurs and professionals are swept aside, and to the resulting nameless class which will be in a position to accept whatever prizes are offered whether they be in cash or kind.

It would take thirty more years for this prophecy to come true. Now, with hindsight, we recognise that the pro/amateur divide twinned with 'the Corinthian spirit' was aimed at cementing the class superiority of a minority of privately funded Toffs over the majority of wage-slave 'Oiks'. Corinthianism was behind the myth that underwrote Baron de Coubertin's revival of the Olympic Games in 1896 (crucially the year before Corinthian Bidlake abandoned road racing). The Baron assumed that those inspirational ancient Greek athletes were strictly amateur, sporting gentlemen, jolly good types like himself and his cronies. How wrong he was, according to a Channel 4 TV documentary shown in July 2007 (*The Ancient Greek Olympics: Playing to Win*). A few competitors were amateurs, but most were full-time professionals exploiting their talent for material gain. In fact, amateurs and professionals competed together then just as they do now.

So Percy was right. But at the time he was condemned by the RTTC whose devotion to Bidlake's Corinthianism was their principal justification for opposing unity to the last ditch (as anyone like myself who was 'banned' for mixing with semi-professionals well remembers).

> The NCU and the RTTC were never friends. The RTTC were particular bastards and they had so many clever men in the top echelon, many more than the NCU. They were steeped in the tradition of time trialing and what it stood for and they wouldn't budge a jot or tickle. (Les Woodland, *This Island Race*, 2005)

Stalemate Renewed

Increasingly, as the power of the League stalwarts was diluted by ex-NCU incomers, Stallard lost his overriding influence and became one voice amongst several. *The Leaguer* sought a fair balance of opinion and weren't averse to criticising him:

> There is a malignant ulcer prevalent in the cycling world common to all three racing bodies in this country. It is the taint of vanity and culminates in the clash of personality. (*The Leaguer*, 1954)

The charge of vanity, here aimed at Stallard and Co., shows how far the political compass had swung since 1942. It raises the question of when, if ever, a matter of principle becomes mere vanity.

In the March 1954 issue, Bill Thompson, a member of the tripartite agreement negotiating committee, was given right of reply. He rebuffed Stallard as best he could by stating that his mandate had left ample room for concessions. Nevertheless, Stallard won the argument and was voted onto a new and more radical negotiating team.

In hindsight, neither man need have worried, because as the months became years and negotiations remained bogged down it was clear the agreement in its present form was going nowhere. The main blame for this must rest with the NCU. Time and again it backtracked on promises made to the UCI, principally on the clause permitting

BLRC licence holders to race abroad. This was its trump card and the only way it knew to control its shrinking membership. Sharing the international racing licence would be to concede legitimacy to the League. Left with the rump of track racing, it would have signed its own death warrant. Thus, dishonourably but pragmatically, it never ratified the agreement.

As the decade advanced and neither unity nor agreement seemed to be getting any closer, frustration mounted. Here in July 1955 the BLRC secretary writes an open letter of complaint to his rivals that they are in breach of UCI rules:

NEW NCU/RTTC MENACE

I have been instructed to write and say that we understand that the NCU and RTTC have recently taken certain action against a number of BLRC members who have competed in an event run under the rules of the BLRC.

We shall be glad if you will advise us – through me – at the earliest opportunity on what grounds this action was taken. As both the RTTC and NCU permit their members to compete in BLRC events, it follows that there must be tacit recognition of the rules of the BLRC by both bodies.

As these rules conform with those laid down by the UCI, it is difficult to understand how the action of declaring certain BLRC members as 'non amateurs' can possibly be justified. The BLRC on its part places no embargo on its members from belonging to, or competing in, events run under the rules of either the NCU or RTTC and makes no attempt to interfere in any way with the rules of these two bodies and we consider that the bi-lateral action taken is entirely out of order.

The BLRC is always ready and willing to meet both the NCU and RTTC for the purposes of reaching an agreement and ending the unsatisfactory position, which, incidentally, is becoming serious. The present situation is due solely to the bi-lateral action of the NCU and RTTC in firstly withdrawing from the Joint Agreement of 1953 and from repudiating the agreement reached on January 2nd 1955.

If you now feel, as we do, that something must be done in the interests of the sport to reach agreement, I am ready to arrange a meeting to this end.

Again, whilst it appears the League strives for agreement, the other two bodies play the wrecking game.

Prophet of Doom

That was one sort of 'menace'. Yet another was identified in a letter from B.L. Jennings of Brentford (April 1954) who warned against rejoicing at the mass defection of NCU members to the BLRC. He pointed out that the bigger the membership, the more the value of a racing licence would be diluted:

> Last season we saw events where something like 120 riders entered for events for which the organiser could accept only 40. This year the number of events has not increased in proportion with the increase in membership . Should we rejoice over the fact that many of the League's former antagonists, good riders though they may be, will be preventing those enthusiasts who gave the League their support when it was most needed, from following their chosen sport?

Former NCU clubs switching to the League had been accused of not pulling their weight. They wanted their share of road racing without the trouble of promoting races themselves. The problem was most acute amongst 3rd category riders, of which there were many. It did not affect me personally. As an elite rider I was assured of a place in almost any Independent / 1st category race I chose to enter. But the dilution of the BLRC posed a far worse threat, as Jennings pointed out:

> Rather than the League becoming the major organisation, it would be quite possible for the newly affiliated NCU clubs, still with strong Union tendencies and with little or no loyalty to the League, to vote the BLRC into affiliation to the NCU. Are the real enthusiasts to be ousted by those who violently opposed and now only wish to dabble?

A take-over from within was then a distinct possibility (rather on the lines of the take-over of Labour in 1994 by the Blairites after the death of John Smith).

Officialdom's repeated failure to reach agreement increasingly prompted voices of frustration from the ranks, as Dennis Mann's poem 'Coureurs' Dilemma'(August 1955) makes clear.

A racing cyclist friend of mine
Once told me this strange tale
As we swapped some yarns and anecdotes
And drank a glass of ale.

It seems that once he'd had a dream
'Nay a nightmare 'twas,' he said,
Mad visions passed before his eyes
As he lay upon his bed.

'Twas not of winning pools he dreamt,
Or having sixteen wives,
Nor of grande affaires d'amour
In high class Paris dives.

But yet it seemed impossible
This dream of his so fair.
''Twas something that the future holds
And perhaps not even there.

And so at length he told me
Of the subject of his dream –
One body to control the sport
And keep it nice and clean.

There only was one licence
One affiliation fee,
To cover all the cycling sport
The road, the track, T.T.

'Just think of it, old pal,' he cried,
'It's what the lads desire;
But now my dream is fading,
It's on the funeral pyre.'

I sympathised and told him that
His ideal could come true
If only they'd take action
And play hell with their H.Q.

The 'heads' they are complacent
Don't seem to care a hang;
'You've got to wake them up,' I said,
'And wake them with a bang.'

Protest now, both loud and long,
Send letters here and there,
Voicing your opinions
And then perhaps they'll stir.

This dream of yours is common sense,
Or so it seems to me;
So why not press for one rule book,
Control and licence fee?

And so I left him to his thoughts,
Ambitions, fate and dreams.
But whether he'll do what I said
Is doubtful, so it seems.

This poem undoubtedly expresses the majority viewpoint, whilst also highlighting the complacency of rank and file cyclists themselves, especially amongst the RTTC. But to call all the heads 'complacent' strikes me as inaccurate and unfair. As I have shown, the BLRC were far from complacent. They seemed much more aware than their rivals of the Home Office's threat to the sport if the dispute were allowed to fester and they strove wholeheartedly for an agreement with honour. The problem was the RTTC who saw nothing in it for themselves and were supported by a large membership who seemed either against or indifferent to reformation and, it has to be said, sat on their hands and did nothing.

By 1956 the 'dilution' of the League began to have practical consequences. In a snub to the memory of the founding fathers, *The Leaguer* was re-named, less provocatively, *The Racing Cyclist and Cyclo-Cross Journal* ('Britain's only road racing paper') and printed in larger format. Though the magazine mix stayed much the same, editorials became less partisan, dispensing with former Stallardist radicalism.

Another symptom of backdoor NCU influence was raised even as late as August 1958 under the heading 'Road Racing Under BLRC Rules'.

The National Secretary has been in correspondence with police authorities recently in connection with incidents which have occurred during races run under League Rules. From this correspondence it has become apparent that far too many Section officials are writing to the police with reference to such incidents and are using the term 'massed start'.

It must be realised that the term 'massed start' ONLY applies to events started or run on totally enclosed circuits, and this term MUST NOT be used in connection with road races starting on the public highway. In connection with these events, it must be clearly pointed out to the police concerned that the riders start off in two lines and that such racing be defined as 'en ligne' racing. References to the term 'MASSED START' must cease at once.

There was a further question mark concerning the legality of a notice to spectators printed in one race programme. It began by requesting orderly behaviour (i.e. 'Please keep to the pavements.'), but ended with a threat: 'Severe action will be taken by the officials if the above notice is not obeyed.'

Again the National Secretary had to step in to warn officials that they had no right to threaten 'any member of the public with any sort of action.'

The BLRC had always prided itself on its self-discipline and such lapses caused it acute embarrassment. Where could use of the term 'massed start' have originated if not from former or present NCU members (in the period leading up to amalgamation, a common rules-of-racing handbook was being shared)? Post 1959, sloppy race promotion was to become a hallmark of the new regime.

Endgame

The years 1955-7 marked the beginning of the end for the League as the groundswell of grassroots opinion grew for unification at any price. By 1957, frustration over failure to 'heal the split' came to a head with the formation of a new pressure group, the British Cycle Racing Movement. The entire front page of the March issue of The Racing Cyclist covered the BCRM's 28-point plan to produce one single controlling organisation by 1958. Whether the NCU or RTTC gave it equal coverage is doubtful. However one clause of this proposal proved significant, 'the formation of a Federation named temporarily The British Cycling Federation with membership for all in BLRC-NCU-RTTC affiliated clubs.' That 'temporary' name was to become permanent and signalled a complete break with the past when adopted by the new unified body in 1959.

The door was closing on the glory days of the BLRC, but some individual members remained dynamic to the very end. Enterprising activist Dave Orford, concerned by the damage done to the professional and Independent classes following Hercules's withdrawal from sponsorship, devised a more affordable scheme to bring in cycle retailers and smaller manufacturers the likes of Wilson Cycles, Elswick Hopper and Langsett Cycles as well as extra-sportive sponsors such as Ovaltine and *The Racing Cyclist Journal* itself. He fathered the sort of club and team sponsorship that we take for granted nowadays but was then anathema to the anti-Independent NCU/RTTC axis. His intention was to keep professionalism alive by providing a stepping-stone for amateurs to take their chance in the part-time paid ranks. He went even further by creating a representative organisation, The British Professional and Independents Cycling Association, to speak on their behalf and a Saturday afternoon race series to give employment to the so-called 'second division' of 'also-rans', a chance for them to shine whilst the stars rested before taking part in the Sunday classics.

Not only did Orford give semi-professionalism a new lease of life, but he also paved the way for the first 1958 Milk Race with his groundbreaking approach to the Milk Marketing Board. Handed this crown jewel of sponsorship on a plate, the BLRC rejoiced and as a conciliatory but rather pointless gesture offered to run the first edition under joint rules with the Union (as the Union had copied BLRC rules, there was effectively no difference in the two rule-books). But when Orford informed Chairman Eddie Lawton that he had plenty more ideas where that had come from, he was warned to keep his nose out. So far and no further – Lawton was busy cosying up to the NCU for the backroom deal that would guarantee him top job upon amalgamation. (He lasted just one year in the post before being replaced by a former NCU official).

As for the 'mag', it survived just long enough to report on the vote for unification and its last issue in January 1959 carried the following statement:

This Annual General Meeting of the British League of Racing Cyclists agrees that all assets, liabilities, obligations and commitments of the British League of Racing Cyclists shall be transferred to or handed over to the British Cycling Federation as from the date of the incorporation of that body.

Ironically, all this happened at a time when the NCU was on its knees, having officially ceded all massed-start rights (including closed circuit racing) to the League. And Stallard may have been right in saying amalgamation was unnecessary, because the Home Office now had its wish to deal with a single road-racing organisation. Left to its own devices, the NCU would have died of natural causes. But with total unity the objective, seven of the 'diluted'BLRC regions demanded a vote and in the interests of democracy could not be ignored. According to Charles Messenger, who said the League had been sold down the river, pro-NCU backroom forces were at work and the stalwarts were out manoeuvred. The vote was carried.

Sadly, correspondent B.L. Jennings's warning had come of age. The influence of the newly promoted 'dabblers' was to be long lasting and deeply damaging. In his preface to *Where There's A Wheel* the late BCF honorary vice-president Chas Messenger, under the heading 'Rape of the League', described the bitterness and recrimination surrounding that final Special General Meeting of 12 October 1958 where the unification vote was carried against the stalwarts' minority wish. Written ten years after that momentous decision, his words make a fitting epitaph not just for the BLRC but also for the journal that had begun its life in 1949 as *The Leaguer*.

Within its ranks the BLRC had people who had the courage of their convictions; who were not afraid to call a spade a spade; who sunk their own identities for the sport; who worked miracles to establish road racing in this country – in the face of what was without any doubt whatsoever, the bitterest struggle in any sport in history.
Amen to that.

The Fruit of Amalgamation
At this time, apart from the Stallardites, few could possibly have guessed what amalgamation would bring, how British road racing over the years was to be shrivelled by top-down neglect and inaction to the point where its survival at grassroots level was in question. It seemed the BLRC had won the battle but lost the war. It was not BLRC dynamism that survived this shotgun wedding but the old Union policy of laissez-faire. Jennings's dabblers, whose distastrous

dabblings wrecked the *Daily Express* sponsorship of the TOB, had become the unambitious masters and instead of building on their inheritance of a solid and vibrant road racing structure, they appeared quite happy just to tick the boxes.

The BCF hit rock bottom in 1996 following the election to president of would-be reformist Tony Doyle and the subsequent in-house coup staged by board members to remove him. An investigation by journalist Ian Bent on Radio 5 triggered a highly critical statement in Parliament by cycling MP Jon Trickett when the competence and integrity of this Sports Council funded body was publicly called into question. Taxpayers' money ultimately had to be squandered to resolve the dispute. An internal audit revealed 'a grave state of affairs' and concluded that the board 'is failing to operate properly and effectively as an executive body'. Even more damaging in terms of Britain's reputation abroad was the damning verdict of UCI president Hein Verbruggen. He lamented the fact that (after 37 years of the BCF) cycle racing in Britain was so undeveloped, causing would-be sponsors to turn their backs and look elsewhere. 'Great Britain is,' he said, 'a completely black spot in the international cycling market.' Again, it seemed Stallard, fervent internationalist that he was, had been proved right.

There have been four important crossroads in UK's cycling history occurring in 1897, 1942, 1959 and 1996. In my opinion, on only two of these occasions have we taken the beneficial path. When a group of reformers led by Brian Cookson took control of the BCF after 1996, they were shocked to discover just how bad things were.

As well as the personality clashes (in the former BCF), the most pressing matter concerned the running of the Manchester Velodrome. More than ten years on, Cookson, sitting in his office in the velodrome, can afford a wry smile as he notes, 'People don't realise how close this place came to being bankrupt and closed down. Within a few weeks of Peter (King) and myself and the new board taking over, it became apparent that this place – which was being run as Manchester Velodrome limited, a wholly owned subsidiary of the BCF – was not washing its face. There was a big outstanding bill for gas and electricity – about £130,000 – which Manchester City Council agreed to cover for us. If that hadn't been covered then we'd have been bankrupt. The padlocks would have been on. I'd say we were within ten days of that happening. This place would probably have been turned into a B&Q warehouse.*

One could, of course, joke that that enormous BCF gas bill was the product of all the hot air generated in the run-up to the Doyle scandal.

In the effort to distance itself from this catastrophe and make a fresh start, the reformers dropped Federation from the title and became plain British Cycling (BC), a move prompted possibly by (New) Labour's tactic of 1994. Indeed, if in 1997 the reformed BC had needed a campaign song then 'Things Can Only Get Better' would have done nicely. By 2002/3 things had got better, significantly so. But just how far progress would continue to the glorious drum-roll of Beijing and beyond, with cycling enjoying such national and international prestige and becoming the darling of the funding agencies, few if any people at the time could have guessed – except perhaps the new administration itself. Success did not happen overnight or by accident. There had to be a plan and a strategy to deliver it. But even foresight was not enough. The plan had to be made flesh and driven forward by ambition, self-belief and ruthless determination – and for that we have Cookson and his backroom team to thank, not to mention the coaches and scores of volunteer assistants.

Time to Acknowledge the Debt

But wait, isn't this where we came in with the BLRC of 1942? Weren't they also largely unpaid volunteers, ambitious and hungry for change, and with a plan? But unlike BC who had money, real estate and support to make their dreams come true, BLRC idealism was thwarted by an intransigent opposition and lack of cash and influence.

As a child of the League, my prime interest is with road racing and whilst I was out of my seat last summer applauding our track stars, I have to admit it was Nicole Cook's two gold medals, Ben Swift's 4th place in the 2008 U23 World Championship and Cavendish's sprint victories in the big Tours that gave me the most pleasure. I also obsessively follow the fortunes of our young team at their BC

---

* *Heroes, Villains and Velodromes: Chris Hoy and Britain's Track Cycling Revolution*, Richard Moore, 2008, p101

training Academy in Italy and of all those other youngsters who, like myself in earlier days, are striving to make a go of it, either with the aid of the Rayner Fund or independently on the Continent. As for our Sky-sponsored road team set to contest the Continental Tours and Classics in 2010 – even Stallard at his curmudgeonly worst would have found it hard to quibble, though he might have questioned whether the policy was not somewhat askew – all fur coat and no knickers.

Which takes us back to the question of our inheritance from the BLRC, founded, let us remember, 'to encourage and promote in Great Britain all forms of Amateur and Professional cycling based upon international practice.' Under BC administration most forms of cycling have indeed been vigorously promoted. The poor relative until very recently has been grassroots road racing, seemingly in slow decline to a rump, the fear being that, whilst the elite flourished, the lower orders might be forced back into the 1930s of closed circuit racing and track.

Now, at long last, after almost fifty years of heads-in-the-sand, something is being done to arrest this decline. Already work was afoot before April 2008, when the excellent Peter King appealed to the government to show more support for sports events on UK roads*. Whilst this move may have been prompted more by embarrassment over the 2007 Tour of Britain being halted in North Yorkshire than concern for the plight of the grassroots, at least it was a step in the right direction – and most people would say not a moment too soon! But, suddenly, matters have taken a dramatic twist with news of a massive grant of £24.3 million from Sport England (thanks to the work of BC's CEO Ian Drake) half of which is to be allocated to domestic competition.

Now Drake wants to build a network of more than 50 dedicated closed circuits around the country and to create a new Sporting Events on the Highway Unit to secure bike racing's future on public roads. (*Cycling Weekly* editorial 01/01/09)

In the flush of recent success and with the 2012 Olympics on the horizon and an obesity time-bomb ticking throughout the nation, BC

---

* See BC website 28/10/07: 'BC lobby government over highway access'.

has seized the day. There could never have been a better moment to influence government agencies on the importance of vigorous exercise on the open road. The threat to road racing remains, given the enforced cancellation of recent Premier Calendar events.

I also would add that never has there been a better time to look back to road racing's roots in the UK not with recrimination I express but with wonder and gratitude. The spirit of the BLRC evinced in Messenger's words has never been extinguished amongst its former adherents. At rallies and reunions greybeards like myself congregate to talk of times old and new and I am always struck by the underlying tone of enthusiasm, fervour, passion, loyalty – call it what you will – that still exists for the League. Almost without exception we are 65 years or older, and whatever we have done since, it is that little bit of character-forming 'Life on Mars' with its jazz and youthful rebellion, penny-pinching austerity and National Service, that remains most vivid in our minds. A few, like Doug Gifford, have carried that fervour all the way to the doors of death. Doug and his brother Alan (Derby Mercury RC) figured large in the BLRC East Midlands Section. Doug died in 2006 and, as his strength faded, he reached out to hold his brother's hand, murmuring as he did so 'Up The League!' Those were his last words.

Most cyclists aged under-60 will find it hard to identify with this 'out of the Ark' sentiment. Why should they? They were not there at the time to experience the vicissitudes. They never had to fight to establish road-racing on these shores. It was their inheritance and handed to them on a plate. It is now a given, and many know not whence it came. But this does not mean that in happier times they are free of debt and should have no conscience. The DNA of the BLRC is in every racing cyclist's blood, whether they recognise it or not.

2009 marks the 50th anniversary of the BCF and it is understandable that the new administration does not intend to celebrate it with any great fanfare. According to Brian Cookson, celebrations will be scattered and muted. After all, little in the name of new initiatives happened in the first thirty-eight years, 1996 left a scar and there is not much to be proud of unless you count Stallard's formation of the now-flourishing League of Veteran Racing Cyclists in 1986 which the dear old BCF, true to form, opposed at the time.

In my opinion, BC has only one account left in the red and that is to the BLRC. The Committee, justifiably flushed with success, might wish to forget it or kick it into touch. It's all water under the bridge – why rake over old embers? The answer to that lies in two words. Justice and Truth. An Inconvenient Truth perhaps to our present administration. Nevertheless, there is nothing clever about playing politics with the truth. To my best knowledge, no public gesture of thanks has ever been made to the League itself as a whole, to those several thousand members who handed on to the BCF the blazing torch of progress. I suggest that now is the hour for that debt to be honoured; for such action, in all honesty, after fifty years, cannot be labelled divisive in the way it might once have been under the old BCF. (Cycling Time Trials, formerly the RTTC, might also like to examine its conscience for the wrecking role of its forefather in the 1940s and 50s – a name change is no absolution).

I have appealed personally to Brian Cookson to take action this year. And not by faint praise. Let it ring out. For, if not, future historians of British cycling will certainly want to know the reason why.

Just look at the crowd! Ken Russell outsprints Nev Taylor in a Sheffield road race.

WARSAW–BERLIN–PRAGUE 1956

During the autumn and winter of 1955 I basked in the glory of my unexpected victory in the Tour of Britain. I was in demand as guest of honour and after-dinner speaker at cycling festivities and appeared on the GB Components stand at the Olympia Cycle Show, signing autographs and shaking hands with everyone's then hero, World Sprint Champion Reg Harris. Even at work my achievement had been recognised. My colleagues had followed every twist and turn of the race in the press and were now profuse in their congratulations. The boss called me upstairs to his inner sanctum and shook my hand awkwardly (a gesture normally reserved for his superiors), informing me that my 'sporting prowess had not gone unnoticed by the Powers that be at Head Office'.

I raced four times that autumn after the Tour and was placed fifth, fourth and third (twice). Any thought of easy victory was stripped from my mind as I discovered what it meant to be a marked man. The mere act of tightening my toe-straps was enough to cause panic in the bunch. In breaks, team mate Dick Bartrop and I were expected to do most of the work, whilst chasing groups drove themselves to frenzy in efforts to bring us back. It was no use complaining (though we did, long and loud). It was a fact of life that we had to come to terms with.

The racing season over, I resumed weight training coupled with sorties on the bike of just over 100 miles per week. Yet despite maintaining fitness tickover, when I restarted racing in March/April 1956 my form was indifferent.

I was relieved I'd resisted the temptation to turn professional immediately after the Tour. Hercules had given up sponsorship and several other manufacturers were following suit. The cycle trade was undergoing cyclical decline and, in the climate of uncertainty created by the continuing battle between NCU and BLRC, sponsorship was hard to come by. Some professionals tried to revert to Independent and compete in mixed-category races. This was more than the RTTC purists could tolerate and they began banning riders who contravened their strict definition of amateur, naming and shaming them in the pages of *Cycling* magazine. My name, alongside all my Falcon Road Club team mates, appeared on this ever growing list. Some of us were double and even triple-banned.

Amidst the internecine strife, the League's membership expanded whilst the Union's declined. The last shot the NCU had in its locker was international recognition. You needed an NCU racing licence to race abroad in events held under UCI rules. The Union's dirty tricks department, getting wind of a BLRC team in a foreign race, would rush off a telegram to the organiser, threatening to report his infringement of rules to the UCI. This shameless blackmail almost always succeeded. Brian Haskell, 1955 winner, was forced out of the 1956 Tour of Ireland after four stages following NCU intervention. Increasingly, a BLRC licence became unacceptable outside the British Isles. The crowning blow came when the invitation to the Warsaw–Berlin–Prague, Europe's premier stage race for amateurs and independents, went to the NCU. The League was indignant: after all it was they who had first patronised this race and provided the overall 1951 winner in Ian Steel. Now they were sidelined and snubbed.

Regarding performance, I was not surprised when the NCU picked me in their team for the 1956 Peace Race. Most top riders had dual affiliation. I'd won the 1955 Scottish Three-Day in NCU colours and my performance in the BLRC Tour of Britain marked me out as one of the best stage riders in the country. Nevertheless, the TOB had been an unmitigated League success and had humiliated the NCU because it demonstrated they had been wrong to oppose Stallard's introduction of Continental-style road racing in 1942. Without admitting to their error of judgment, they set about organising their own road races after the 1951 TOB.

However, performance was one thing and politics another. I had competed in the TOB as an 'Aspirant', a hybrid category that was neither amateur nor Independent, but somewhere in between, a category the NCU/RTTC did not recognise. Moreover the RTTC had banned me. I imagined this would be an irreducible problem and that I'd blotted my copybook with the NCU for good. So when the Peace Race invitation flopped through my letterbox, it came as a shock. All I had to do, apparently, was resign my Aspirant category, not difficult in the circumstances, and revert to amateur. Only later did I discover my amateur status wasn't a UCI problem, but entirely home manufactured: there were lots of Peace Race riders whose amateur status was more questionable than mine. As for Iron Curtain riders, East Germans, Poles, Czechs, Russians and so on were state sponsored and professional in all but name. Shamateurism was alive and well in the 1950s, even inside the ranks of the RTTC.

My preparation went as well as could be expected. I battled on through the usual attack of springtime bronchitis and my training mileage bore comparison to previous years for that point in the racing season. I completed the 4-stage Tour of the Border, achieving third place in the time trial at Selkirk and fifth on GC behind winner Brian Haskell. In other road races, I had a second and third place, and in my last race before the WBP was deprived of certain victory by being sent off course close to the finish. Though I lacked the astonishing early season form of 1955, I wasn't in bad shape when I met up towards the end of April with the other team members at NCU headquarters in London.

Stage one winner, Tour of the Borders, 1955

The first edition of the Peace Race had been in 1948. In fact, it consisted of two separate simultaneous seven-stage races: one from Prague to Warsaw, won by Alexander Zoric and the other in the reverse direction from Warsaw to Prague, won by Augustin Prosenik. Both men were from Yugoslavia, the only occasion that nation has ever supplied a winner. Zoric was handicapped by having been seriously injured in 1945 during a bombing raid on Belgrade when he lost an eye. But all the competitors were handicapped by having to race over roads left in appalling condition by the war in Eastern Europe. Some idea of how tough it was can be gleaned from the fact that of 56 starters from Prague only 29 finished in Warsaw, and the average speed for the 1104 kilometres was a mere 19 mph.

The races caught the popular imagination. People filled the stadium venues and thronged the routes. The two sponsoring newspapers, *Rude Pravo* and *Glos Ludu*, saw their circulation double, but even they might have been surprised when, within a few years, this amateur race with such humble and parochial beginnings had grown to rival the big three European Tours. The 1956 version was the first to have the full blessing of the UCI and as a consequence a record entry of 141 riders from 24 countries.

With typical press hyperbole, our 1956 team was described as the strongest ever sent to compete abroad. It consisted of Stan Brittain, Owen Blower, Don Sanderson, Dave Tweddell, Jim Grieves and myself, with Jim Allan as mechanic and Bill Shillibeer masseur. Stan was the obvious choice for team leader. Following his splendid third place in 1955, he was tipped both here and abroad as a potential winner. Owen was also a previous finisher and he and Stan had formed a close-knit friendship. The manager, A. J. Spurgin was a bit of a joke. Typical of much NCU top brass, his racing experience was limited to closed circuits and the track. Putting such an ingénu in charge of a team competing in the biggest amateur stage race in Europe seemed extraordinary, but the pool of managerial talent in an organisation that had shunned road racing for 60 years was obviously very limited. The UK's top managers, Bob Thom and Percy Stallard, were ideal for the job but, sadly, disqualified by their BLRC connections.

This was my first trip abroad and I was excited by the prospect of travelling to the communist East, where few Westerners had got to tread. Our chartered KLM flight touched down in Amsterdam to pick up the Dutch and Belgian teams. A small hold (most cargo then went by sea or rail) meant seats had to be removed to accommodate all the bikes and spare equipment. The ideological Cold War between East and West had gone into an even deeper freeze when the USSR laid siege to Berlin in 1948 with an armoured cordon around the city, only broken by the Berlin airlift. But with Stalin's death in 1953, tension eased and this marked the beginning of commercial flights to the East. However, I'll never forget the frisson that passed round our cabin when the captain announced over the intercom, 'We have just entered Soviet air space.' We were blips on Soviet radar and possibly were being shadowed in the air to make sure we didn't veer off the agreed course to indulge in a spot of photographic espionage. Poland, like every other Iron Curtain country, was under the armed umbrella of Russian military might and I just hoped someone our side had remembered to send its MIG squadrons a postcard of a proletarian dove of peace perched on a bicycle saddle.

We made a bumpy landing on a near deserted aerodrome where a huddle of pre-fabricated huts, not unlike military guardrooms, served as the passenger terminal. Our last view of the West had been the sleek, neon lit foyer of Amsterdam airport, with showcases crammed full of Cartier and Rolex watches, Chanel No. 5 perfume, jewellery, cameras and other consumer goodies. Now it came as something of a culture shock not to be greeted on the tarmac by a posse of journalists and a brass band, as I had fondly imagined, but rather to be ushered into the presence of grim-faced officials in a barracks of bare boards, blank walls and trestle tables for our visas to be scrutinised and the contents of our suitcases turned over with something approaching contempt. Suspicion hung heavy in the air. In the background I noted armed guards with pistols at their waists. It was hard to believe we were here at the Poles' own behest for a so-called Peace Race.

Stan had advised me to take something to trade or barter in exchange for a classic Leica camera, the one thing worth bringing back home, he said. On his recommendation I'd packed several pairs of ladies' nylon stockings and an enormous quantity of razor blades, all purchased in the Sheffield branch of Woolworth's and supposedly in short supply in Poland's inefficient state-run economy. Now these were tumbled out onto the table with all my other belongings and segregated for close inspection by a butch female official. At sight of the shaving accessories, the hairs of her nascent moustache twitched in pleasurable anticipation. She exchanged words with an interpreter, who stood behind, hands crossed over his crutch as if to ward off a free kick in the penalty area. He indicated the nylons.

'Are these for your personal use?' The precise, accented voice was heavy with sarcasm.

I played a straight bat. 'No, they're intended as gifts.' And realising this still left space for doubt, I added, 'For ladies.'

'So, you have come to Poland to meet ladies. I thought it was for a bicycle race.' He stared at me stonily before pointing to the blades.

'And these?'

My brain went into overdrive before I hit on the obvious answer. 'Cyclists shave their legs.'

He gazed nonplussed at the enormous pyramid of Wilkinsons. 'How many legs do you propose to shave?' he queried. 'All the legs of everyone in the race, by the look of it.'

Fortunately, I realised, it was not so much an accusation as a joke. And he was so delighted with his own little joke that he immediately translated it for grey-uniformed Miss Butch, whose lustful black eyes crossed and re-crossed from razor blades to nylons and back again. How tempting, these symbols of capitalist decadence! If only she dared confiscate them without creating a diplomatic incident. I imagined bristly plantations of unshaven leg hair thrusting against the thick grey serge of her trousers. She waved me through. Scooping everything back into my cheap, cardboard suitcase and snapping it shut, I felt like one of those Oxford Street pavement traders shamefacedly caught in the act and being moved on by the cops.

Things could only get better and fortunately they did. Outside, representatives of the organising committee were waiting to greet us and amidst handshaking and backslapping we climbed aboard the bus that was to take us to our city centre hotel. En route, crossing the suburbs, came another cultural shock: mile upon mile of identical concrete tower blocks, like tins of Spam stacked up on a shop shelf, housing the regimented proletariat. At the time it looked brutal and authoritarian. Little did I imagine how soon these inhuman-looking excrescences would begin to sprout in Britain, first, ironically, in Sheffield, my home city, with Park Hill Flats.

The Hotel Warszava offered more surprises. Double doors served entry to large, airy and scrupulously clean bedrooms with tall double windows and, puzzlingly, no bed blankets but a sort of bulky eiderdown (the duvet, unknown in Britain), all to keep at bay sub-zero Polish winters.

I looked out onto the centre of Warsaw, most of it reconstructed to replicate its pre-war appearance after being razed to the ground by the retreating Wermacht S.S. in 1944 as a last vengeful act of spite.

The Russian team was billeted just across the corridor, and I half expected to meet some reserve or even hostility, given the way they'd been brainwashed to despise Westerners. But they turned out to be like cyclists everywhere, cheerful and friendly, squashing our hands in their bear paws and roaring, 'How do you do, Englishman?' We swapped club badges. Our lightweight, hand-built bike frames with delicate lug-work were objects of fascination, theirs by comparison looking crude and heavy, as if constructed on a Friday afternoon from off-cuts in a Siberian tank factory. Maybe they were speculating on how long our flimsy machines would withstand the battering of Polish cobbles. Rumour had it that the Belgians inserted strengtheners of broom handle down their head and seat tubes and I wondered had the Ruskies done likewise.

From his appearance, their burly team manager might have been one of those statuesque Heroes of the Soviet Socialist Republic cast in bronze. Hearty 'Ivan' tested my bike by swinging it up in the air and crying 'Zooooooooom!' as though to hurl it from the window to see if it would fly, whilst from a safe distance our more gentlemanly Captain Mainwaring of a team manager winced with disapproval as Ivan exploded into laughter and nodded reassuringly to his team. Perhaps, with us observing, he was striking the first blow in the battle of psychological warfare – or maybe it was just the vodka, his breath seemingly on permanent, high-octane liftoff.

Whatever, the Russians were well prepared to ride the race as a team. The results speak for themselves. Between 1956 and the mid-sixties, under their world famous coach Leonid Selesnev, they would win the team race seven times, the individual race three.

Meals were taken alongside other teams at a nearby restaurant. A small national flag demarcated each table. Ultra-slow service was the order of the day, the sullen staff's leisurely approach suggesting they were under orders to treat us as unexpected guests parachuted in from an alien planet. A hundred and forty starving racing cyclists trapped for an hour or more in a stuffy basement, with nothing to placate their gnawing bellies but brackish bottled water, soon lost empathy with Comrade Waiter. The noise level increased with the length of delay, and the arrival of food at long last united the diverse nations in ironic cheering. Then it was some inedible muck of fatty mutton, potatoes, cabbage and rough salty bread, much of which ended up on the side plate. There was no fresh fruit and in the end, to add fibre to my diet and avoid constipation, I resorted to purchasing some sour scabby apples from a street vendor outside.

Stan had warned me of shortages behind the Iron Curtain. Yet it still came as a shock to walk the streets and see vast empty department-store windows entirely devoid of display, as if recently looted. Everywhere there were queues for basic foodstuffs. The drabness of daily life was worse than anything I could remember from even the darkest days of Britain at war.

I bartered my razor blades and nylons for a German Foth-Derby camera at a main street photographic shop. The jumpy shopkeeper bolted his door to do the deal, his desire to possess these Western 'luxury' commodities only just outdoing his fear of the authorities. What if I were a government agent masking as a foreigner to entrap him in a bit of undercover spivvery? The camera proved to be in good working order and I was soon taking snaps. It is now a classic of 1930s vintage and worth much more than I gave. And yet now, I am beset with curiosity. If only this thing of metal and worn dimpled leather could speak, what a tale it might tell about the fate of its previous owners. Somehow it had survived the Nazis' invasion of 1940 and the almost total destruction of Warsaw in 1944 as they retreated. Yet the Foth-Derby factory in Berlin had not been so lucky and never reopened following the 1945 devastating bombardment of the city, which left it in ruins.

Each night shady characters tapped at our doors with offers on everything we possessed, even the clothing we stood up in, evidence of a thriving black market. In Prague, at the end of the race, Don Sanderson, tired of being pestered, sold his bike and 'some other bits and pieces' and used the currency, worthless back home, to buy a couple of cameras, one a twin lens Reflekta 11. The other he sold in Britain for £100 at a time when he was earning less than £10 per week, this dodgy but toasty deal dropping into his lap butter side up.

When I showed Stan my camera, he said I'd been too hasty and would have done better dealing for a Leica with one of the spivs, and he was probably right.

It was all a bit creepy – spivs materialising out of the night and demanding to know in heavily accented broken English if we had anything to sell. It was somehow reminiscent of a scene from 'The Third Man', set in post-war black market Vienna, or Roman Polanski's 'Ashes and Diamonds', dramatising Warsaw's resistance fighters battling the Wermacht S.S. from their underground hide-out in the sewers. It was easy to recall the savagery of that struggle and how some of the worst twentieth century atrocities had taken place here beneath our feet in the recent past. The devastated city had been rebuilt in pre-war replica to overlay the bloodstains, but there remained in people's eyes an antiseptic sadness. Though eleven years had elapsed since the evil Nazi magician was roasted in his bunker, Poland was not yet free. Under *de facto* Soviet rule, it had merely exchanged one dictator for another.

Training was also bizarre. After breakfast our team would line up in the street outside the hotel accompanied by a police motorcycle and sidecar. Stan and Owen, relying on memory, led us over the cobbles and out of the city, our bikes being jumped across the tramlines. The police followed. Once through the suburbs we met wide, concrete highways and as our tyres engaged with the interfaces, the recurrent thumping and vibration through saddle and handlebars became like Chinese water torture, so that we almost wished ourselves back onto the less predictable cobblestones. In four days we covered 165 miles, mostly in rapid *en-ligne*, bit-and-bit sorties to alleviate the monotony of that dead-flat landscape, ideal for battling tanks but for cyclists bum-numbing.

The countryside was eerily deserted, almost no motor traffic apart from military convoys. In fact, with every level crossing and crossroads having an armed guard – bored, rifle-slung conscripts agape at our unexpected apparition – and few visible signposts, it was as if Poland was on a permanent war footing ready to repel a capitalist invasion. Every so often out of the shimmering distance would emerge the black dot of a plodding horse and cart, its muffled peasant driver crossing herself as we overlapped, presumably to ward off the evil eye of those who arrogantly assumed freedom to cycle over the People's Plain. Indeed, despite state paranoia and years of atheistic dictatorship, religious symbolism was still everywhere evident in the form of iron crucifixes and roadside shrines sheltering blue and gold plaster Madonnas and vases of fresh-cut flowers.

Increasingly, the police escort tagging behind us became an irritant. What were they up to, we wondered? When asked, Spurgin couldn't say. The charitable explanation was that they provided backup in case of mishap or us getting lost. But my imagination took its own paranoiac course: surely they were there to keep us on the straight and narrow? They might fear us poking our noses into some secretive, military-restricted area and reporting back to MI6 on our return to Britain. They might suppose one of us was actually a spy masquerading as a racing cyclist. No foreigner could possibly have more liberty than us to travel wherever and whenever we wished and indulge in a spot of on the ground nose-poking. Were our hotel rooms bugged? Had the secret police planted informants amongst the staff? If so, what had they made of those shady characters treading a nightly path to our doors?

Perhaps more to the point, the police escort made us feel like school kids on a supervised outing. One day we took revenge. At Stan's instigation and without prior warning, we did a sudden U turn, throwing them unexpectedly into total confusion. They skidded to a halt, their engine stalled and they sat there glowering like dummies as we pedalled past them in the opposite direction giving a cheery wave as we did so. This cheeky expression of freewill must have shocked them to their authoritarian core, because seconds later they whizzed past us in a huff, heading flatout for Warsaw, and they never accompanied us again.

Attached to our party were two Poles: Stani, the interpreter, and Anna, a sort of liaison officer there to ensure we followed to the letter the social and cultural programme prescribed for our visit. Both were a constant source of amusement. Blonde-haired comb-wielding, Stani fancied himself rotten, forever admiring his own reflection in mirrors and shop windows. Pretty Anna got awfully flustered if we fell behind schedule, blaming Stani, since she could only communicate with us through him. Stani was disdainful; privately, he boasted of his excellent record for bedding 'the young ladies' and forecast Anna would shortly be added to his tally. Sure enough, on the eve of the race, he appeared smirking at breakfast, claiming to have scored. This might have been just an empty boast, yet for us red-blooded male celibates it represented an enviable free and easy attitude to sex that would be absent in the West until the Swinging Sixties.

Top of Anna's agenda was a visit to the Palace of Culture. This towering, fortress-like showpiece of Stalinist architecture dominated the Warsaw skyline. Inside, it was full of echoing space, grand balconies, stone stairways and statuary. Anna explained it had been a post-war gift from the Soviet people to the Poles in recognition of their eternal friendship. Out of earshot of the suited minders skulking in the shadows, Stani was more forthcoming. 'Gift my arse!' he said. 'We call it Stalin's eye. It's there to check us out and remind us who's really the boss in this country of ours.'

Stalin, that multi-million serial murderer three years dead, was still knocking on his coffin lid. In Poland, I discovered hatred of the Soviets ran as deep as hatred of the Germans, and it wasn't hard to understand why. The Nazi/Soviet pact of 1939 had agreed upon a joint invasion and division of the country, whereupon Poland would cease to exist as an independent nation. The Soviets had set about converting their half of Poland to communism. To achieve this, they arrested over 10,000 of the professional and intellectual elite and then liquidated them all in an appalling assembly-line massacre in the Katyn forest near Smolensk. A bullet in the back of the head at the rate of 500 a night, it took the NKVD, garbed in leather butchers' aprons, three weeks to complete their bloody work. One of these butchers later went mad and shot himself. They used German Mauser pistols throughout so as to blame it on the Nazis. The advancing Germans later dug up the bodies and put them on display to the world to justify their propaganda picture of the Russians as sub-human beasts. Each side blamed the other. It got worse. As the tide of battle turned, the Russians re-captured the forest and again disinterred the bodies, falsifying the evidence date-wise to 'prove' they were not involved, and threatening the original witnesses to force them to change their stories. This was the work of Poland's 'friends'.

But that wasn't all. Much later, in the final stages of war, as Hitler's army faced defeat and the partisans attacked from out of Warsaw's sewers, Stalin ordered his divisions to delay their advance until the Wermacht had crushed Polish resistance and blown up half the city. This made the subsequent imposition of Soviet authority so much easier. It was a history of cynical exploitation, betrayal, barbaric cruelty, slaughter and destruction – hard to equate with eternal friendship!

Something happened at one of our evening engagements to demonstrate this undercurrent of hatred. It was a dinner in our honour at a printing factory in the suburbs of the city. As we entered the bedecked foyer, confronting us was a semi-circle of girls, dolled up in their best attire. Stani explained, smirking, that we were each to choose 'a pretty lady' to partner us at the dining table. Anything less PC is now hard to imagine. It was like *la choix* at a Parisian bordello.

There was no way of knowing whether these girls were volunteers or commanded by management. The occasion passed with uneasy laughter and what the rejects felt like I can't begin to imagine.

My choice fell on a shapely girl with a wonderful smile and laughing eyes. She exuded confidence. Her name was Barbara (Basha for short!). During the meal I choked over a glass of 'water'. It was colourless liquid from a carafe, actually of vodka, and she could hardly contain her amusement. Afterwards she took me by the hand, still spluttering, on a sightseeing tour through the darkened factory, and on a metal gangway above a workshop with its machinery silent under leather wraps, we kissed. It was so sexy being far away from home in this foreign country and embracing a strange girl in the mysterious half-light of an empty factory. Neither speaking the other's language made the kisses seem even more illicit and daring. Alas, there was no time to linger. We would soon be missed in this land of eyes and ears where every move was noted. We scribbled our addresses on factory card and, using sign language, promised to correspond.

Dinner at the Warsaw printing factory:
(l to r) Don Sanderson, two Polish girls, the author and Basha

Returning to the party we encountered a fair old hullabaloo and a shove and push fracas. Angry voices were being raised in Polish, English and (bizarrely) German. Our mechanic, Jim Allan, was sandwiched between two hefty Poles, who were threatening to knock his head off. It seemed the vodka had flowed too freely and his insistence on communicating with his hosts in the German he had learned as a POW had opened up some festering wounds. It took the intervention of an official to calm things down. He reminded all present that the British were honoured guests: after all, we had kept faith with Poland in 1939, opposing Hitler's invasion by declaring war on Germany. I realised then that this feeling of debt and gratitude, despite our subsequent desertion of their cause in the post-war carve up of Europe, was what lay behind the great warmth of our welcome from the ordinary people of Poland.

One morning we were all whisked off to a health clinic in the suburbs to be weighed, measured and tested for cardio-vascular efficiency. It was, we were assured, simply to ensure our fitness to survive the world's toughest amateur cycle race. But I have since wondered if there wasn't a hidden agenda to discover if our superior Western living standards had given us an 'unfair' advantage in athletic performance? It is hard to believe such statistics were not conserved and shared throughout the Soviet empire. To 'ensure a level playing field', the East Germans would later begin their infamous routine doping programme.

May Day was the second biggest holiday in the Soviet calendar. Stani and Anna ushered us out onto the packed streets to witness the lengthy passage of the May Day Parade, part folk pageant, part showcase for the Communist Party and military. For most of the populace, the holiday continued through the next day. Not for us, though: it was now our turn to be paraded. We marched beside our bikes, behind the Union Jack, around the cinder track of the immense Warsaw Stadium, almost deafened by the applause of 100,000 spectators. Somewhere high up on the terraces amidst this enormous congregation was Basha, snapping us with her camera. Then the race began: stage one, the 112 kilometres circuit of Warsaw.

Spring had arrived overnight. The sunlit, tree-lined avenues were bud-bursting green as 144 riders from 24 nations sped by, bumping over concrete interfaces and shuddering over pavé, leaping tram lines, brushing past banks of spectators leaning out at a dangerous angle as if to catch our hot breath. Massed ranks of support vehicles, press and team cars, conducted their own tyre-squealing rally in hot pursuit. It was my first experience of the lunatic continental bike race. At one point we hit an ancient square embedded with immense cobblestones, like a field of giant granite mushrooms, worse than anything in Paris-Roubaix. It was like trying to race across the Devil's Causeway. From 30 mph, our speed collapsed almost to walking pace and some riders were left waving for assistance, holding ready-to-reassemble kits of tubing that had once been bikes. No doubt to 'Ivan's' surprise, my lightweight Langsett and I survived unscathed to finish in the bunch, 53 seconds adrift of Italian stars, Bruni and Cestari. It was a good beginning for us all, apart from poor Jim Grieves, who crashed at the stadium entrance and finished a little off the pace.

That evening, I began to develop stomach pains, perhaps from something eaten at the printing works dinner or one of my scabby apples. No one else had complained, but I felt sick and lacking in appetite. Bill Shillibeer advised drinking plenty of bottled water and letting nature take its course – which it did in the form of a well-trodden course to the squatter.

I slept badly and next morning felt even worse. Forcing down some breakfast, I joined the others for the 90-mile stage to Lodz. A strong breeze was blowing at right angles to our route, shaking trees and kicking up mini dust devils around the many building construction sites of new tower blocks. Once out on the wind-lashed plain, I found myself buffeted into the left-hand gutter, racing flatout just to maintain contact. The back wheel ahead seemed to offer little shelter. It was like doing a solo time trial in the middle of a road race, a doomed enterprise as I quickly recognised, growing progressively more exhausted.

My befuddled brain attempted to make sense of it all. Why was I struggling today when yesterday in the city streets I had ridden so easily? I was tagged up behind a short ragged line of riders just back of a score of others who had formed two parallel diagonals across the full width of the carriageway, the front ascending into the wind, the rear descending towards me, an unbroken loop of movement. From my exposed position, their performance looked effortless, and I cursed those easy riders in the back line, who periodically sat up and freewheeled, nonchalantly taking a hand off the bars to drink, whilst I crouched in the aerodynamic horizontal and pounded the pedals at a speed I knew was impossible to maintain.

British team (l-r Tweddle, Sanderson, Hewson, Grieves, Blower and Brittain)
Warsaw Stadium

Stage one. The British team
waits outside the Stadium

Then it clicked: of course, this must be an echelon! Why hadn't someone warned me what to expect? The echelon formation to combat a crosswind was a bread and butter tactic of continental racing but forbidden on Britain's open-to-traffic roads, where only *en-ligne* racing on the left was permitted. Apart from seeing photographs in *But et Club*, it was totally outside my experience.

But it was one thing to realise my error, another to rectify it. Joining an already established echelon was easier thought than done. There must have been six or seven of them, covering perhaps half a mile of road from first to last. From a helicopter overhead they would resemble the seven multicoloured sails of some great, elongated ship-of-the-plains, tacking into the wind, and I was swinging on a fool's rope, exposed to the breeze behind echelon number three. I summoned up my reserves of strength and sprinted up behind the rear line, trying to force a way in. Impossible! There was no gap. It was jam-packed tight, pedal-to-pedal, gutter-to-gutter. My attempts at infiltration, judged dangerous, met with curses and back-swinging elbows and the door remained firm shut. For a minute I clung on in the sideward blast of air, hoping for the miracle of a gap to open up of its own accord. When none did, my strength gave out and I dropped back.

Peace Race? It was open warfare!

I sensed the echelon behind was about to vacuum me up. My legs drummed with pain. Panic set in as I envisaged myself falling through the entire field, from echelon to echelon, until I was in the last, smallest, weakest, or off the back altogether, alone.

My salvation came with a whirr of wheels. An East German rider sprinting out of the saddle lunged past and closed with the echelon that had just cold-shouldered me. He yelled something to another East German, who leaned into and held up the descending line, creating a slither of space just wide enough for his team mate to slip into. Other riders remonstrated angrily as the squashed line wobbled on the point of crash before suddenly stabilising and resuming its former clockwork progress.

So that was how it was done, with the aid of a team mate.

But now I realised that this rider must have vacated space in the echelon behind, and, sure enough, swallowed up in its forward rush, breathing in tight, I filled the gap he had left. Immediately I felt the pressure come off my legs, the relief as much psychological as physical.

At last I was in from the cold, integrated into a group, which, though divided by nationality, was fired by common purpose: to catch the echelon ahead and stay clear of the one behind. Ironically, in this land of the communist collective, our dog-eat-dog pursuit resembled nothing more than the proverbial capitalist rat race, attenuated here and there by touches of corporate comradeship.

This Devil-take-the-Hindmost at 25 to 30mph endured for as long as the crosswind blew. On a highway compass-needle straight, over featureless plains, it felt like forever. You lost all sense of being an individual and became instead a cog in a revolving machine. Repetition ruled: rider after rider clicked up the front rank to the top of the echelon, shouldered the sudden weight of wind, performed a few brisk pedal turns, then slipped thankfully backwards into shelter, snatching a drink or bite to eat on the way down. In the gutter came a little sprint to regain the front rank and repeat the process: again and again.

Sometimes an extra strong gust provoked a chain reaction, the entire line swaying as if in some presentiment of the Mexican Wave. Despite fatigue, you had to stay electrically alert. There was no room for error. Any clash of wheels or pedals, entanglement of handlebars and you'd bite the concrete, bringing down others with you in a groaning heap.

Cycle road racing is unique amongst athletic sports in the lengthy demands it places on concentration. Even seasoned commentators who stress the physical strength and determination of competitors underplay the mental pressure. To be a great athlete and tactician is not enough in the peloton's packed ranks. Ancillary skills are required: the whiplash reaction of the racing driver, the balance, timing and spatial judgment of the trapeze artist.

Now each little sprint to rejoin the front rank was sapping more of my precious energy, already depleted by the stomach bug. Yet any delay invited being shoved out by my neighbour in line, whose allegiance was first to his team, then to the merciless machine, the echelon of which he was part. A tired rider who missed his cue to join the front rank might be displaced back down the gutter, with little hope of regaining his position.

Which is exactly what happened to me long before Lodz. Losing my place in the echelons, I lost 25 minutes. The smooth concrete highway had given way to rounded granite cobbles, with lacunas the size of tank traps. I ended up a pale ghost of a rider with a raw arse, toes skinned and bleeding, and so shaken I felt in immediate need of masseur Bill Shillibeer to reassemble the separate parts. My guts were rumbling painfully and the race doctor ordered me straight to bed without food. Dave Tweddell, also suffering from a stomach disorder, had finished just behind me. Owen Blower had had a near miss in the bunch from a metal fragment resulting from someone's gas-inflator bouncing from its clip and exploding on impact with the road. A dent in his top tube was worryingly close to the saddle crutch area.

Next morning I felt well enough to eat breakfast and inside the first 30 miles of this 130-mile stage had joined a group including Stan, Dave and Owen in what was to be the day's good break. But soon diarrhoea reasserted control and I was forced to stop and dive into some bushes, to the merriment of a gaggle of peasant spectators. I had come well prepared with a pocketful of toilet paper and emerged clutching the remnants just as the bunch rolled up. They pointed and laughed. Somehow they found the idea of someone breaking away for a crap enormously comic.

Owen and Dave were both dropped from the break, which was caught six miles from Stalinogrod. The Italian, Bruni, chalked up his second win and the Rumanian Dimitrescu became race leader with Stan equal third.

Survival was now top of my agenda. Until I was rid of this strength-sapping illness, I couldn't begin to race. If only I could survive the next day's 112-mile stage to Wroclaw, I might recuperate on the rest day. But another problem had reared its several ugly heads in the form of saddle boils. How I longed to quit the *pavé* and ease my backside out of the saddle on some nice, long hills, but none was scheduled until the fifth stage to Gorlitz.

Somehow I got through the next day, finishing midfield 78th and losing a mere 11 minutes on the Russian winner, Kolumbet. Don Sanderson, increasingly confident, was 20th, nearly a minute ahead of Owen and Stan, whose frame had broken. Jim lost 34 minutes and Dave, 50 minutes. The stage, conducted at high speed, had ripped the field apart.

Wroclaw, like Warsaw, also had a history of Nazi atrocities. There, on the rest day, politics intervened in cloak and dagger fashion. We had an unofficial invitation to meet 'some ordinary Polish people' and were whisked out to a grim apartment block somewhere in that forbidding, industrial city. The flat and its care worn inhabitants, with whom we shared some grainy ersatz coffee, was drab with scarred, paint-peeling walls..

'The Party want you to see only the best side of Poland,' we were told, 'but this is the reality. Working people live from hand to mouth. They possess little or nothing. They are like slaves in their own land to the real masters, the Russians. When you return home, tell your people the truth. Don't forget us!'

It was like being visitors inside a gigantic prison asked to carry messages to the free world outside. I realised then how lucky we were to be born citizens of the West. The Peace Race encompassed more than sport: it was part of a long propaganda war being waged between opposing ideologies.

Wroclaw–Gorlitz was the only stage I can honestly say I enjoyed. The race quit the plains and entered wooded hills, not unlike the Scottish Borders. The rolling roads were well surfaced with very little pavé and the weather sunny and warm. It was a delight for once not to be struggling to stay in contact. I was climbing with ease, and with the stomach bug in abeyance, finished comfortably in the bunch at Gorlitz, where East German star Schur won in his homeland.

But it was a false dawn. Next morning I woke to rain pitter-pattering on the roof tiles. Outside it was cold and miserable and we faced a long, flat stage over more bone-shaking pavé to Berlin. The diarrhoea had left me feeling weak, but saddle boils had become a big problem. Yesterday's hilly stage had brought temporary relief; now my rain-soaked shorts were chafing and I wriggled painfully around the saddle. Even that became too much and I had to rise and dance on the pedals. My arse felt as if it was being put through a carrot grater and that evening when I removed my shorts they were caked in dried blood. Racing became impossible and, after 30 tortured miles, I abandoned and climbed into the sag wagon. There, to my astonishment, sitting on the wooden bench seat and swathed in blankets were Dave and Stan. They had beaten me to it.

Now as the bus bumped its slow laborious way on the remaining 100 miles to Berlin, we cursed those stubborn, tail-end riders, who, with no time limit to concern them, refused to abandon. Whenever one gave up and clambered aboard the sag wagon, he was cheered like a hero. Nevertheless, tracking the last man, we arrived, frozen stiff, some two hours after the winner. At least we were to be flown home next day, unlike previously when those who abandoned had to trail the race in buses all the way to Prague.

That night was the best and worst. Abandoning a big race, you begin by experiencing overwhelming relief. Then doubt sets in. The painful ordeal is mentally re-ordered to a minor inconvenience and you begin to question your tenacity. 'If only I could've hung on for just a little longer –'. You feel guilty for abandoning your comrades and letting down friends, family and supporters back home.

But one final concession lifted our spirits. Lodged apart from the teams in a small guesthouse rather than some anonymous hotel, we took full advantage of the licence to wine and dine at the organisers' expense. The good German beer flowed, Stan's scouse wit was caustic on aspects of the race and officialdom, and with two cheeky Belgian comrades, we made merry.

So for me ended the Peace Race – disappointment salved with laughter. It was an experience not to be missed. Few ordinary people got to see life at first hand behind the Curtain. It was an education in realpolitik, if nothing else.

Jim abandoned later. Owen only just hung on through illness to finish 50th. The great revelation, though, was Don Sanderson, 20th overall and brilliant winner at Tabor, Britain's first ever stage victory in the Peace Race. I was delighted for this BLRC rider. He had come a long way since I beat him into third place in the National Junior Championship of 1951.

Don Sanderson comments

Don was one of the movers and shakers of early 1950s' road racing. He had the ideal, robust physique for a tough race like the WBP and was a good sprinter and climber. Alongside riders like Dick McNeil, Bill Baty and Norman Purdy, all from Tyneside, he had learned how to 'mek it gan up the hills!' and you had to grit your teeth to stay with one of his attacks. Amongst many races that he won was the now classic Tour of the Border. He also won the final Wolverhampton–London stage of the 1955 Amateur Circuit of Britain, in which overall victory went to the talented Desmond Robinson, Brian's brother. Not surprisingly, he quickly caught the international selectors' attention and was picked for the World Championships in 1954 (Solingen) and 1955 (Frascati), as well as the 1955 Tour of Egypt and Tour de la Meuse. One high status race that still troubles his thoughts was the ill-fated Tour of Ireland, when a snowstorm forced 94 riders to retire in a single day, leaving only 17 to complete the course. 'I was twelfth,' he comments modestly. 'It sounds better than fifth from last.' This was the infamous Irish Tour when a break of three riders rounded a bend at full speed to be confronted by a horse and cart. In the ensuing crash one rider was impaled on a wooden shaft and died on the spot. The horse in a panic raced off towards the approaching bunch. 'It was an horrific sight, the horse and cart galloping towards us with this rider still impaled on the shaft. I've never been able to get it out of my mind. And, for some reason the race went on almost as if nothing had happened.'

About the 1956 WBP: a newspaper article before the team embarked read, 'These riders have been training arduously whenever possible, and nothing has been spared to see that they have had the facilities necessary to bring them to peak fitness at the right time.' I have to smile at that. What facilities? There weren't any. I was as green as grass. My training for every race was the same – plenty of miles up to March, then out with the local 'blind': 30 to 40 of us having a mini race over about 30-plus miles each Tuesday and Thursday night after work, when the riders you had beaten in the weekend race got their revenge. The only advice I remember getting for the WBP was beware of the cobbles, and so my special training was to spend extra nights alone riding round and round six miles of cobbled roads alongside the river between Newcastle and Wallsend.

My first memory of Warsaw is going out training for the first time over some of the worst of these cobbles and my front wheel collapsing, a sign of what was to come.

Much of the race remains a blur in my memory, except the day I won. More by good luck than good management I must have hit peak fitness, because I felt so strong I could have been sitting on a motorbike. You will have had that feeling when you know you should win the race, but nothing is guaranteed. You probe and probe to see how fit the opposition is, but you don't want to get rid of them until the time is right. It was a hilly stage and I was in a three-man break. Towards the end I attacked and managed to shed one rider. But with only two of us left it became more difficult and it was only by taking chances on the final descent that I managed to open a gap. I held this slender lead through the streets of Tabor. Then there was a difficult twisting entry to the stadium. When you have someone just a few lengths behind, you take those unfamiliar final corners with your heart in your mouth, knowing that you have to take risks to win, yet if you make a mistake and fall badly, you might not even finish second. That is some adrenalin rush!

On rest days we were invited out to dine at the various sponsors' factories. Attending the final dinner in Prague, I foolishly left the hotel without any means of identification. When the dinner was over, instead of travelling back with the team, I walked a young lady home. I then had to find my way back to the hotel, walking through a deserted Prague after midnight with nothing to prove who I was and unable to speak a word of the language. The only other persons around were soldiers or police in twos with guns over their shoulders. These days it will be difficult for younger people to imagine what it was like behind the Iron Curtain and how the authorities distrusted Westerners. Maybe it was the darkness preying on my imagination, but suddenly I became very afraid that I might be arrested as a spy and 'disappeared', never to be seen again. I have never in my whole life since felt so happy to see the doors of a hotel.

Gil Taylor comments on the 1959 Race:

During the course of the race an abscess appeared on my crutch and by the time I reached Gorlitz it had swelled up to the size of a small egg. I started the stage to Berlin, but after riding 100 miles out of the saddle, it became impossible to carry on and I had to abandon. The race doctor insisted on sending me off to hospital to undergo an immediate operation in case blood poisoning set in. In the operating theatre they spread my legs apart and hauled them up in the air on pulley ropes. Then they put a sort of wickerwork mask on my face with a cloth over it on which they poured some ether. I don't know why they used this instead of some more up-to-date anaesthetic – perhaps they thought bike riders were super-tough. Anyway it didn't work. 'Count to ten,' the doctor said. I was still counting at 35 when they must have lost patience and begun the operation. I recall my eyes watering somewhat.

Afterwards I spent a few days recovering on the ward. A young nurse was assigned to dress my wound. She didn't know I'd studied German at school and I didn't let on because I liked trying to translate the conversations that went on around me. One day she said to a colleague, indicating me, 'If I climbed into bed with him, do you think he'd give me a ruby?' She must have seen my passport where it had my profession down as 'jeweller'. I was very tempted to say, 'Jawohl, meine frauleine!'

A RACING CYCLIST'S WORST
NIGHTMARE

Does the subject of cycling ever intrude on your dreams? In that shifting landscape of disconnected shapes and forms you enter each night does the bicycle ever figure large? If so, you might well ask yourself why.

For long after I quit racing in 1960, my dreams remained in a cycling-free zone. It was as if for twelve years my actual life had been so stuffed with the gristle and bone of competition that my dream life had decided enough was enough. It could cope with no more. The time had come for a rest, to take a break from bicycles and anything so connected. Wasn't there plenty more for my unconscious to be getting its teeth into? Unresolved conflicts from childhood and adolescence, for example, or my sleeping mind's peculiar insistence that I was an underground member of an armed gang, pretending to be their friend and ally but in reality awaiting the moment when I could usefully betray them – a dream I still enjoy from time to time as the images shuffle round to the front of the queue for my twice nightly viewing on the cerebral screen. Yes, enjoy! It should be the classic nightmare, but it isn't. Throughout I am expert in disinformation and the use of lethal weapons, including the garrotte. Bullets fly and blood is spilled and whenever my own life is in danger or true identity threatened with disclosure, I never hesitate to kill. But like secret agent Bond, whatever the perils, I am ultimately in control and never experience anxiety or fear or wake up in the proverbial cold sweat. No, that was something being kept in reserve for the time, many years later, when the cycling dream slithered up out of some temporal wormhole and gradually, through repetition, assumed the ugly proportions of nightmare.

To begin, this is what you know. It's the morning of the biggest bike race in your life. It's taking place in some foreign country far from home and you don't speak the language. Not a single word. Otherwise you think you're well prepared. You've done all the necessary training and the mechanic has checked over your machine and given it a complete bill of health. You watched him do it. So what can go wrong?

You're in a hotel room all to yourself. But you're not alone. The rest of the team is just down the corridor – at any rate, you hope they are because, putting your head round the door, you observe that the corridor seems to have no bounds in the known universe: it just goes on and on into a black dot of infinity.

Never mind, you say to yourself, it's time to go down to breakfast and you're bound to meet with the others there. Beneath your tracksuit you're already dressed for the race. You even have on your cotton cap all ready for when the start flag drops and the director's lead car pulls away. You begin descending the staircase to the foyer, carrying your sports bag in your left hand with the bike hanging from your right shoulder. It's one of those wide, sweeping 'Gone with the Wind' staircases and after a time, tottering from step to step, you think, 'This is daft! Why don't I just get on my bike and ride?' So you do. You balance the bag on the handlebars and just go wheeeeeeeeeee like a kid sliding down a banister. At the bottom is this big, semi-circular desk where a bellhop in a pillbox hat is standing in as receptionist. You hop off the velo and do a breakfast-eating mime because otherwise, being a foreigner, he won't understand. He points towards the dining hall.

So far it's just been a pleasant little interlude in your life, but this is where it starts to become dark and disturbing. The gloomy, half-lit dining hall is deserted. There's no sign of your own team nor any other. You can see evidence of a meal having been eaten recently: crumbs on the tables, half empty carafes, screwed up serviettes, loads of dirty cups, glasses and plates waiting to be removed. But where are the waiters? Ah, see – one lurks in the shadows – and there, he's just putting out all the lights. What? He can't be. It's too soon and you haven't eaten. You go over and do the mime for breakfast, but he just shakes his head and taps his watch. He seems to be saying it's too late.

Too late? The clock indicates eight-thirty and the race doesn't begin until eleven. So where has everybody gone? You shrug your shoulders and spread your hands the French way. But again the waiter shakes his head. You point to the clock. Have they brought forward the time of start? Even if he understands, he won't say. All he does is scowl and keep tapping his watch.

You begin to feel anxious. No breakfast, no food in your belly and two hundred kilometres to race on an empty stomach. Now you're not even sure what time the race starts. Your team and manager seem to have disappeared off the face of the earth. Have you been forgotten, abandoned? Have they gone without you? Was there something you missed at the briefing? Well, at least you can have a warm-up. At once the thought of doing something positive and you feel better.

You dump your bag and tracksuit in the foyer and clamber onto your bike. The staircase is steep, but in bottom gear you overcome it and climb back up to the corridor on the floor where your room is situated. And there the corridor is transformed into something like a town centre race circuit with four right angles. You pedal hard and brake at every corner, pedal and brake. Round and round you go, time and again passing the top of the staircase. Now you must take care as obstacles begin to litter your path: mops, brushes, trolleys, Hoovers, soiled bed linen. The cleaners are hard at work. It must be later than you think.

At the end of every straight is a floor-to-ceiling mirror and you can observe yourself crouching low over the bars, your image magnifying to fill the glass as you approach. Then swish! You make the turn and race towards the next mirror. Mirror after mirror. Image upon image. You flick through this photo album of mirrors and see your picture reflected back at you again and again.

Suddenly, another rider appears ahead and you give chase. Trouble is you can never quite get close enough to see him whole and complete. He's just bits and pieces: here a back wheel, there a saddle, now a part of a leg, and always just disappearing round the bend in front. Try as you might you can't catch him. Which is truly awful, because if only you could, he'd surely tell you where the race started, at what time and, most importantly, how to get to the rendezvous.

With no one to ring the bell on this *perpetuum mobile* pursuit, you go faster and faster until, in a whirling frenzy, you crash through one of the mirrors and land in the street below with barely a jolt. Now facing the hotel entrance, you want to get back inside to claim your bag and tracksuit from the foyer. But all the doors are locked and when you rattle them a flashing red sign reads, 'Hotel Access Denied.'

Things have gone from bad to worse. You're alone in the middle of a big foreign city with time running out on starting the bike race of your life and now your access to your sports bag containing your passport and cash has been denied. You're penniless with no proof of identity. There's only one thing left to do: you must try to find your own way to the start.

You look left and right. The street is deserted. There's no one to ask for directions even if you could speak the language. But, at that precise moment, a paper bag bowls past on the breeze. You follow and it leads you off the main road and into some seedy-looking backstreets where half-clad women hang over balconies and threatening groups of young men are gathered on the street corners. It's a high crime area. Now you're really scared. Your bike is all you have, your sole means of escape. Your anxiety forces you to sprint, whilst at the same time you realise that on an empty stomach and with a big race in the offing, energy is something you can ill afford to waste.

At last you sprint free of the mean streets, evading all those clawing, grasping black-gloved hands trying to pull you down and you're into the city centre, riding down a wide boulevard. Tall buildings loom at either hand, shadowy without detail. Somewhere a clock booms the hour. Eleven o'clock. That can't be right. It seems barely five minutes since you were back at the hotel, doing circuits in the corridor. Perhaps your mind is playing tricks? Another clock strikes. Nine o'clock. That's more like it. You can still make the start with time to spare – if only you can find the route.

You decide to head west with the rising sun at your back and your own long shadow cast ahead as a pointer. Your confidence begins to return. But suddenly the way ahead is barred. Behind wooden barriers, workmen in leggings are raking steaming black tar right across the highway. You have no choice but to turn around. It's then you observe the three men in dark formal suits, wearing sunglasses and walking with the self-assured swagger of very important people on a duty of inspection. They're crossing a wide, empty market square dominated by a tall, forward-leaning, concrete building in the form of a clock face. A semi-circle of armed bodyguards tails them, carrying automatic weapons. The tubby man in the middle with his broad colourful sash looks strangely familiar – of course, the waiter from the hotel. And now you understand – he must be the race director and these are VIPs reconnoitring the area being prepared for the finish. You drop your bike and run towards him, calling, 'Please, sir, which way to the start?' He gives a scowl of recognition and taps his watch. And then the bodyguards push you aside and he's gone.

Gone. And, as you turn around to claim your bike, that too is gone. It was lying in the roadway where you let it fall and now it has disappeared.

The situation is desperate. You're stranded in a foreign city far from home without clothes, apart from your racing gear, and with no cash or means of identification. You're hungry. You're due to start soon in the most important race of your life, but you've been deserted by your team – and now your bike has been stolen, your most precious possession, your passport to freedom. You've no means of escape. You're lost and utterly helpless. And you cannot speak the language.

At this point you hear the roar of engines. From a side street a posse of motorbikers emerges. They're all dressed in black balaclavas and leathers. Are they here to police the race? No, because they point their machines towards you and rev up. Behind their goggles you glimpse cruel, merciless eyes. They must be out to run you down. You're rooted to the spot with fear as they race towards you, closer, closer, until the zigzag pattern of their tyres blots out the light. Then, falling through darkness, your legs flailing, you suddenly awaken with a sharp intake of breath and lay blinking in the sunlight.

Thank God! It was only a dream. You're sweating and your heart is thumping against your rib cage and there's still a whining sound in your ears, but at least you're safe at home in your own little bed as the morning sun streams into the room through a crack in the curtains.

But this self-reassurance is brief, because the dream hasn't quit and at once starts knocking for re-admittance at the borders of your conscious mind. Your precious bike, you left it in the street and it disappeared. How stupid! And it's not the first time. It's happened before. The same stupid thing has happened over and again in the same stupid dream and you never seem to learn from the experience not to leave the bike behind – your one and only, you have no other – not to drop it in the first place, not to turn your back on it, not to remove it from your sight for a single second. It's almost as if you wanted to lose it. Now you can't just walk away and leave things as they are – you have to do something whilst there's still time. No matter that reason assures you this old vintage bike's locked away safely in the garage integral to your house, just one of three, and all you need do is open a door to see them hanging there. It's not reason that's calling the shots. You're still under the dream's spell and loss is trapped inside your skull and stinging like some enraged wasp. Somewhere back in that faraway foreign city is your bike, and the only way you'll ever recover it is to step out of consciousness back into the dream.

You lie back, shut your eyes and will yourself to sleep. Impossible, and after a time you give up. However, the dream persists long after you've quit your bed. All day long, fragments of it keep intruding into your conscious world – the red-flashing 'Hotel Access Denied', the sneering VIP waiter tapping his watch, the airless corridor of mirrors, the seedy backstreets, smell of fresh-poured tar, humiliation of being abandoned and ignored – and loss – that overwhelming sense of loss throbbing in your head like some awful guilty secret.

In olden times, dreams were often interpreted as communications from the spirit world, ancestral prophecies or warnings, even as one of many and various gods speaking to you personally. Now, in our modern scientific age, we know better. Research under laboratory conditions has revealed that, without exception, we all dream, every one of us, but without necessarily remembering the exact details. A recurring dream, however, through repetition is stored in the memory and becomes a self-fulfilling entity. Sleep is divided into modules of deep unconsciousness, which give way to dreaming as we emerge to full wakefulness. The period of dreaming is observable by means of increased mental activity recorded in the lab on a brainwave monitor and a phenomenon called Rapid Eye Movement.

What is the purpose of dreaming? Psychoanalysts are generally agreed that it puts us in touch with our deepest feelings (the 'id'), which may well be repressed by our conscious mind (the 'ego'). Beyond the virtue of being a treasure trove of creative thought, it may also act as a problem solving laboratory and an emotional safety valve that helps us deal unconsciously with life's pressing issues and so preserve our mental stability. How often have we gone to bed with a problem and woken with its solution? It is significant that people deprived of sleep for long periods (as a form of torture, for example) begin to hallucinate, a sort of second-best dreaming, pointing to its vital role in our human existence.

Time then for us to consult a 'trick cyclist' and have the dream package unwrapped by a trained professional, a therapist. Out will pop a collection of happenings from one's past, but subtly changed and altered to suit a new purpose. That sinister foreign city, for example, isn't that reminiscent of 1950s Warsaw? The missed race may symbolise some desire now totally out of reach and forever unobtainable. Youth? Note too, as the dream unfolds, how the pressure of time increases (the watch tapping, the race deadline), just as you are feeling increasingly abandoned, ignored and powerless. By the end, threatened with death, the only escape is to wake up and re-enter the time-bound real world. Yet even there the theft of the bicycle nags at your mind and cannot easily be set aside. The lost bicycle is the most powerful symbol of them all. Maybe it stands for vigour and freedom, or ultimate escape? Maybe in our final unconscious moments before death, we shall rediscover it on the road to eternity and pedal off into nirvana?

Our psychoanalyst might well conclude that all this manifests the fear of growing old, with accompanying powerlessness and loss of self-esteem. It will end only with one's acceptance of mortality's inevitability.

I must say I haven't had a recurrence of this dream for five years, since I turned 70, which suggests some necessary mental re-adjustment has now taken place. If only I could say the same for that other me inhabiting the id, that fully paid up and armed part-time infiltrator into the twilight Mafia. Yet this is no guilt-ridden nightmare, but more like a parallel universe in which the details are forever changing, and where I lie, cheat and murder at will and get away with it, too. Here I am, like some superannuated Soprano-family mobster, stalking through a thrilling and violent black and white movie of my own making. Such enfranchisement of pleasure without accountability may well explain its longevity in my dreamlife. But what, I wonder, does it say about the hidden me?

Once, long, long ago, I had a girlfriend who shocked me by scrutinising my face and suddenly saying, 'You have the eyes of a murderer.' I was stunned. How had she come by this impression and did she imagine it was a compliment? Violence had never for a moment entered into our relationship. We had never had a quarrel. Needless to say perhaps, the affair was brief. But I have since wondered, did she, through 'the windows of the soul', discover some secret propensity I was hitherto unaware of and have never needed to activate? Or was she merely the soothsayer who gave me the permit to dream my murderous dream?

THE ANATOMY OF A ROAD RACE

Sheffield, like Rome, was built on seven hills. There the comparison ends. The industrialised, soot-blackened, knife and fork capital of my birth was somewhat light on architectural splendour, and its residents so necessarily tightfisted that throwing a coin into a fountain and making a wish would resemble the act, not of a dreamy romantic, but profligate candidate for the loony bin. Nevertheless, this abundance of hills ensured the city's cyclists became well-practised climbers, often with attitude. Talking to them of the Cotswolds, Chilterns, Kentish Weald, any place in the 'soft south', you invited a knowing grin and some contemptuous reference to nursery slopes. Even the Lakes, Northumberland, Yorkshire Dales, Welsh mountains and precipitous Cornwall only bore grudging comparison with their beloved High Peak. It followed that practically every local race was held in Derbyshire. The climbs, descents and brief intervals of flat to recover and plot induced a sort of Victor Sylvester foxtrot rhythm – slow, slow, quick, quick, slow – about as far removed from the quickstep of the Belgian kermesse as you can imagine. In between much watching and waiting – slow, slow – the race would burst into life with very aggressive climbing to pare the bunch down and speedy descending to ensure the dropped riders rarely made contact again. Each lap or new hill and a few more non-climbers pealed off, until only the doyen of mountain eagles remained to contest the sprint finish.

The North Midlands, centred on Sheffield, was one of 21 sections throughout England and Wales under the aegis of the BLRC. In the national race calendar, each third Sunday in August was highlighted as the date for the Section Championship. The senior version was a race of about 60 miles. Wherever this was held, it was keenly disputed, the intense personal and club rivalries being pitted in the struggle to determine who would be crowned amateur champion of the region. Our arena was inevitably the High Peak, for how else but by climbing could a champion worthy of the name be selected? Heaven forbid a contest on some mildly undulating course to the east, where a trackie might win in a bunch dash for the line or, even worse, some 'pathetic' time trialing fiend go it alone, winning on brute strength and 'luck', ignorant of the subtle stratagem of slow, slow, quick, quick, slow that validated the true mountain road race – as some dyed-in-the-wool League men would have it.

The two favourites for our 1953 championship were Sheffield Phoenix's Nev Taylor and John Pound. For a number of years, alongside the Sheffield Racing Club's Derek Hextall and Ken Slater, they had been at the head of local affairs and, despite young upstarts like Dick Bartrop, Peter McFarlane and myself appearing on the scene, had the maturity, strength and experience to suggest this year would be no different. The course was a single, large, out-and-return loop that included three stiff climbs – Moscar, Mam Tor and Froggatt Edge – with some lumpy intervals between that cyclists from Eastern counties might also call hills. It was a stern test and today's racing men who, according to letters in *Cycling Weekly,* phone a race organiser to be sure the course is flat before signing up, would have had heart attacks at the prospect. The headquarters for issue of numbers and bike check was at Hillsborough swimming baths, with the rare advantage of showering facilities. Its fuggy, heavily chlorinated atmosphere upon entry stung the eyes and induced tears, good practice for the leg-cracking trials to come. From there we proceeded in neutralised formation, two abreast, to the juncture with the A57 at Rivelin Valley post office, where the race was de-neutralised and we were let loose on the first climb of the day to Moscar Top.

Moscar is by Peak standards an easy two-miles ascent with an average gradient of about 5%. When legs are fresh it provides little challenge to the conditioned racing man, unless a strong crosswind is blowing across the moors behind Redmires Reservoir. This was a major route from Sheffield to Glossop and Manchester, but with next to no traffic on this overcast Sunday morning, riders could, with care, shelter themselves by straying over the white line. From Moscar Top, the rapid, twisting descent to the vast Ladybower Dam had to be respected, especially in wet weather, when skidding off into the ravine and playing heady or footy with a granite boulder was always a poor second best to staying on road. A sharp left across the dam wall led to Bamford, preceded by a short, steep climb, first throw of the dice for weak riders. But for the most part, all this was just testing the water and the bunch would re-group, holding itself in reserve for the forthcoming ascent of Mam Tor (literally 'Heights of the Mother').

You knew what you were in for the minute you turned right towards Castleton in the Hope Valley. This road was the nearest thing in the Peak to being slow-slow flat, but there ahead on the close horizon arose the imposing, dumpling-shaped 'Shivering Mountain', so called because it was literally in constant motion, periodically burying the main A625 road to Chapel-en-le-Frith under landslips of loose shale.

The section championship was a community race where almost everyone knew every one else and in free time drank and partied together irrespective of club affiliation. It inspired a spirit of participation that sat above competition, particularly amongst those third cats who sensed their number was up when the gradient was up. Amongst the also-rans was sure to be some bright-eyed wag who, seeing the mountain looming, might wail in mock funereal voice, 'Mighty Mam Tor rears her ugly head,' adapting a shock/horror *News of the World* sex exposé headline to comic effect.

William the Conqueror built Peveril Castle in 1080 to subdue the local population – since when Castleton, in its shadow, has become a tourist hotspot with pretty, lime-washed stone cottages and gift shops selling trinkets made from Blue John stone, once mined in the nearby caverns. In the 1950s it was mainly ramblers and day-trippers arriving by coach and train who formed the Sunday press of people on its pavements and gawped at the pack's colourful intrusion up the main street.

A hundred or so pedal turns and you were through the small village and out again onto the A625, with the by now towering presence of Mother Mountain seeming to pull you along the half mile of *faux plat* that preceded the real climb. In its shelter, the prevailing headwind disappeared and the atmosphere might become as still, thick and heavy as a velodrome before the advent of air-conditioning. Now the joking was over and a hush of anticipation (or dread) fell on the bunch, as serious contenders jostled to be among the leaders. It was still a small sprocket job as the pace hovered around 20 mph. Then the road swung sharp left around the horseshoe bend and you were briefly out of the saddle getting the last of momentum from your big gear before changing down for the steep section. All around, sprockets chattered as tension-taut chains sought the lower ratio. There was no secret to making a smooth change onto the large sprocket: simply ease off the pedal pressure as you shifted the gear lever. But there was always someone who miserably failed the test, stalled, wobbled and questioned the sprocket's paternity, as if a good cussing was a wand to wave over the tinny, toy-town derailleur and make it dependable. Meanwhile they regressed to the rear ranks. There, those with their numbers about to be up had forward propulsion problems of their own and loudly objected: 'Look where thart bloody goin', Fingy. Thou'll have us all off!'

A word about gearing: the standard double chain-ring in the 1950s was 52-48. I coupled this with a block (cassette) of 14-16-18-21-24, giving me ten gears with a top of 100 inches and a bottom of 54. I have to say that I rarely used bottom gear in a race unless, that is, I was faced with a hill steeper than 1 in 6, or my legs were giving out after a 100 plus miles and survival was the only realistic option. There were reasons for this. One, I was a pusher, not a pedaller. Two, I distrusted the Simplex derailleur that for one reason or another I employed throughout my career. It was poorly designed. It relied too much on the force of its flimsy spring – and that was always touch-and-go. Sometimes, to attain the big sprocket required several chattering attempts, with a consequent loss of momentum at precisely the time when you most needed not to give an inch to your opponents.

North Midlands Section Championship 1953, MamTor

The photograph shows the bunch nearing the midpoint of the climb. In the background you can see, below, the enormous horseshoe bend. Some riders are out of the saddle, some sitting, but the overall impression is of concentrated effort as someone ahead, out of picture, puts the hammer down. Only stocky Roy Marshall of the Sheffield Mercury spares a half glance for the photographer (Phoenix's Curly Goodrich, who garnered a few precious bob from selling photos to the image conscious) – the rest full focus on the action. This is one of those decisive moments in a race when your heart pounds, your breath rasps, your lungs singe and your legs begin to scream. Doubt can invade your mind. Only you know how much, if anything, you have left in the tank.

Apart from a couple of parked cars far below, the road in this tourist hotspot in late August, close to the famous Speedwell and Blue John Caverns, is blessedly devoid of traffic – just as well, for half the riders are on the wrong side of the broken white line. In fact, I have manoeuvred myself to the far right, close to the 'Danger' sign that alerts descending motorists to the approaching hairpin. From this vantage point I have an unobstructed view both sideward and ahead and can take rapid action in the event of a gap opening up. I must say, whatever I'm really feeling, I do look relatively comfortable and relaxed.

I was 19 years of age, ten months into my two-year stint of national service with the RAF. I was stationed at RAF Stafford, the premier UK camp for cyclists, and had recently finished third in the 5-day, 538-miles Tour of the RAF, behind Joe Christison and Ron Coe. I held a first-category licence. Though but a skinny youth, as behoved someone of high ambition, I had already tested myself in top competition against the Independent class, the best of Britain. I had lots of racing miles in my legs and several long training rides of 160 miles plus. So if muscle has memory I should have had nothing to fear from mighty Mam Tor. As long as I concentrated, made the right moves and Lady Luck smiled, there was a chance I might yet become the youngest ever North Midlands' senior champion.

What happened next? Fast-forward the film twenty miles to the second photograph and we are on the two miles ascent of Froggatt Edge. Here you can see a selection has taken place. Johnnie Pound heads John Short (Falcon) and Dick Bartrop (Rutland CC). I am falling back on the outside after a turn at the front. In the middle distance appears the solitary figure of a dropped rider, whilst half-hidden behind Bartrop and Short may be two other riders about to lose contact. Our postures indicate a sudden surge of speed.

Pound   Hawson   Short   Bortrop.

Climbing Froggatt Edge

A confession: I am not a habitual race-recycler who, by multiple retellings, engraves a story on the brain and recounts it with the vividness of a new DVD. I have only these two old photographs plus a couple or three of my own recollections to piece the tale together. Thus surmise jostles with memory. Just where did the breakaway occur? Probably not on Mam Tor itself, but afterwards on the road from Sparrowpits to Peak Forest and Stoney Middleton. There the prevailing downhill is interrupted by at least one steep ascent, ideal for the swift attack.

And the photograph only tells part of the story. As Curly's shutter clicked on our group, someone out of frame was ahead, leading by about 100 yards. My own mental snapshot shows him launching a sneaky attack on the inside, surprising us all as we climb in single file. Accelerating out of the saddle, his long arms would throw the bike from side to side with tyre-swishing ferocity. The attack has come out of the blue. He has out-thought us. We youngsters never expected this from the gaunt veteran. Rather we saw him content just to do his makeweight bit in the break, gambling on his powerful

163

sprint finish to deliver his second Senior Championship in three years. It is an audacious move on the steepest part of the climb that has caught us napping and before we get our act together he has forced the gap.

The man in question was Nev Taylor of the Phoenix. He was in his thirties and according to contemporary wisdom that meant his star should have been on the wane. But evidently no one had informed him of this fact, for now he was ramping away up the road and we four relative fledglings were making no impression on him.

Nev was both deeply respected and also the subject of comic interpretation by the cycling fraternity. At mention of his name people would quietly smile. He was one of those lovable eccentrics that are the stuff of British legend. He stood well over six feet tall and in conversation would bow slightly to come down to your level. He was a member of the Communist party and could harangue with the best of them in his gruff, unabated Sheffield accent, his long arms gesticulating stiffly, reminiscent of a marionette. Indeed, Disney's 'Ichabod' figured amongst his nicknames, as also did Big Nervile. He was among my pantheon of local heroes and in my estimation hadn't a bad bone in his body.

But launching an attack like this up the tough Froggatt climb with the pace already high was cheeky. He was pushing us to our limit. An excellent time trialist, close in 1941, to equalling the 25 miles competition record, once he reached the summit and got his head down with barely 20 miles to go, there might be no bringing him back. The alarm bells rang. Little wonder his Phoenix team mate, and here rival, Pound, who also aspired to the title, was striving out of the saddle.

During his career, Johnnie, a useful climber and sprinter, won many races and represented England in teams racing at home and abroad. This day I had him marked as danger man number one. Yet in some respects he was Nev's antithesis. In physical stature they were the Phoenix's Little and Large. With his curly black hair, perpetual tan and sunny disposition, he could have passed for a swarthy Italian. And, rare for a cyclist at that time, he possessed a creative intelligence that gained him a place at the Royal College of Art, and he was later to be praised for his embellishment of the royal chair used at Caernarfon Castle for the investiture of the Prince of Wales in July 1969.

We four cross the summit together. Nev's lead hovers at around 150 yards as we begin the descent to the Fox House Inn. I perform a mental calculation involving distance remaining and my latent energy reserves. Do I have what it takes? Can I close the gap alone? I decide to take a chance. I jump, sprinting flat out in top gear and the burst takes me to within 50 yards of my target. At this moment there is a clap of thunder, the heavens open and gross raindrops fall, running sweat into my eyes. The shower is over almost as soon as it begins, but driving hard downhill, blinking and half blinded, I fail to register the significance of the wet road surface, in places slimy after a period of drought. Coming up is a left-hand dogleg over a stone bridge. As Nev brakes, his back wheel skids and he sways this way and that like a tightrope walker in a breeze before regaining balance. I am a less experienced bike-handler, or not so lucky. When I brake a touch too hard, my wheels slither from beneath me. I end up sliding on my side over the gravel and into the ditch. Forewarned, those behind crawl past, and Shorty in passing shouts to ensure I'm OK.

By the time I get to my feet and check myself over – a net of holes in my shorts, blood oozing from cuts on the legs and arms – they are out of sight and, with my fate as warning, the stragglers continue crawling by. I make my way to the finish as best I can, there to discover Big Nervile was never caught and has again been crowned Section Champion. Once more the wily old fox had danced his foxtrot to perfection.

Tomorrow, early morning, I have to cycle the 100 kilometres back to camp. I decide it is best to have my wounds dressed professionally. At the Royal Infirmary a tetchy nurse in the Accident Department scrubs me clean with antiseptic, applies sticking plaster and gives me an anti-tetanus jab.

'So you fell off your bike?' she remarks frostily, consulting the case notes in a way that suggests she has better things to do with her time than patch up careless idiots. As I prepare to hobble out, she puts on her size twelve bossy-boots. 'Just remember,' pulling a disapproving face borrowed from matron. 'Don't go so fast next time. Slowly does it.'

It is fifty years or more since my generation practised slow, slow, quick, quick, slow in the High Peak, and much water has flowed since in and out of Sheffield's many reservoirs. Big Nervile has passed away, a loner to the end apart from his beloved Phoenix, Communist party and Sheffield Wednesday supporters' club. He never married and had no children, but fervently believed in the brotherhood of man. To the Communists he left his house; to his Phoenix proxy-family his money. I salute his memory.

Mass motoring and the Nanny State have done for cycle racing in Derbyshire. As for mighty Mam Tor, the Shivering Mother reasserted her authority when a massive landslip buried the A625 in 1979, just as Thatcher's market-driven philosophy of Me-Me-Me was about to bury the brotherhood of man. Road closed. It has never been re-opened.

John Pound and Nev Taylor on Mam Tor

NUTTERS

At the 46th hairpin on the Passo dello Stelvio comes the moment to launch his final attack. Just one man remains in contention, the rest blown apart by the ferocious rhythm of his pedalling. His shadow cowers beneath him for shelter as the hot sun beats down from a clear, blue sky. Yet racked with pain, he is resolute. Surrender is not in his vocabulary. He rises from the saddle, launching every atom of his being into this one, last, great effort as the gravel road ahead steepens through banks of snow. Then Coppi falls away, haggard and utterly defeated, sliding back through the caravan of following vehicles and press photographers on their brute motorbikes.

Now he is alone, storming up the final kilometres to the summit. And now he descends, crouching low to gain momentum, fearlessly risking his neck on the slithering bends. Then comes his appointment with glory. He enters the town, crosses the finishing line, punches the air. He is the first Englishman ever to win a mountain stage in the Giro d'Italia.

On the podium, he cradles his bouquet. Beautiful girls embrace him. Soft lips leave their fragrant imprint. Cameras flash, immortalising the moment for posterity. The spectators are ecstatic. In thousands they roar his name.

'Ryan! Ryan!'

'Ryan! What the bloody hell do you think you're doing?'

As Sergeant Worthington's voice punctured the daydream, his hand scrabbled across the desk towards the in-tray piled with EM40s that he was supposed to be 'actioning'. But it was too late. 'Sweet FA, Sarge, if you ask me,' leered aircraftsman Furzer, delighted at some light relief to the evening shift's monotony.

'Shut it!' the sergeant yelled, 'Or I'll have you both on fizzers. Why in this man's Air Force am I lumbered with you two National Service pongos? One yaps like a Jack Russell, the other meditates like a monk. When it comes to work, neither of you knows his arse from his elbow!'

'Ciggie, Sarge?' ingratiated Furzer.

Abstractedly, the sergeant took a fag from the open pack of Woodbines and lit up. 'I've been watching you, Ryan, for five minutes, wherein, as your chum Furzer observes, you have hung motionless over that desk like a constipated turd. Tell me, are you paralysed or on vacation?'

'I was just thinking, Sarge,' he blurted.

Worthington – career sergeant and war veteran – removed his horn-rimmed spectacles and fixed Michael with a glare.

'Thinking? With what, pray? You two haven't half a brain between you.'

Furzer tittered, stirring an imaginary spoon.

'You're not here to think, Ryan. You're here to act – on those EM40s , to requisition and hasten supplies of essential aircraft parts to our boys in Korea. There is a war on, you may recall, which if we do not win, hordes of little, slitty-eyed Chinks will overrun our NAAFI and nick your Durex and my fags. Clear, or do I need to spell it out?' He took a long pull on his Woodbine.

'That don't worry him,' laughed Furzer, 'fags and Durex. He's one o' them cycling nutters. He'd be happy enough with a friggin rickshaw as long as it got pedals.'

Michael glanced at the service issue wall clock. Quarter to eleven. The shift almost done. Why had he left it so late to make this tricky request?

'It's like this, Sarge,' he began. 'I've been meaning to ask, only I've got this chitty…'

At this, Furzer, hysterical, almost fell off his chair, while Worthington's Welsh eyes narrowed dangerously as if he'd just smelled an alien fart.

'Chitty? What chitty?'

'It's for a duty supper. Only, the cookhouse closes at eleven prompt, see.' Worthington glowered and Michael wondered if he'd misjudged the moment.

'It's pukka, Sarge. Flight Kowalski signed it.'

'Flight who? Cow what? Are you trying to pull my pisser?'

'No, it's gen,' said Furzer. 'It's that new Polish geezer wots i/c cycling. They don't half con him. He can't speak English proper and he signs for whatever they stick under his nose.'

Despite his sneaking regard for the cockney comedian, Michael sensed an opportunity to get one back on him – and possibly Worthington, too.

'So you can speak English "proper", can you, Fuzzy. That's news to me. But if you can, you have just insulted Flight Lieutenant Kowalski, implying he's a fool. Now if I was to tell him what you have just said, here, before a witness…' He left the threat hanging.

''Ere,' muttered Furzer, 'can't you take a friggin joke?'

As a matter of fact, as Michael knew, Fuzzy was almost right about Kowalski. He was a pushover, but not without good reason. When the C.O's office had dished out oversight of the various sports, cycling was low priority, so they lumbered the Pole with it. No use giving him anything too British, they reasoned, like rugger, rowing or cricket. He was a foreigner, so it made sense to allocate him something Tour de Wotsit 'foreign' and tell him not to worry as it would run itself. Trouble was Flight was a Catholic with conscience and a sense of duty. He liked to do things well. And he had done cycling well, despite, to paraphrase the Sarge, not knowing his arse from a chain ring. From the moment Kowalski assumed duty, Bas, corporal i/c cycling, had bombarded him with requests, which fell principally into two categories: time off to race and train and extra grub from the cookhouse.

The extra rations argument went thus: cyclists pedalled on their stomachs. Camp food was crap. But to make up for its crappiness more of it was needed. 'Excellent! My observation precisely,' Flight commented, tweaking his little black moustache and perceiving the inalienable connection between excellence and nutrition. Duty suppers, duty dinners, even duty breakfasts, all flowed from strokes of his pen, with additional scope in the excellence for sandwiches to consume on training rides and bread, butter and jam to make toast on their return to camp.

Now, for the first time, Worthington found himself face to face with a product of the Flight's excellence as Michael took two crumpled chits from his pocket and smoothed them out on his desk.

'There you are, Sarge. It's all gen. One duty supper chit, one long week-end pass starting at 23.00 hours, which is' – he glanced again at the clock – 'in ten minutes time when we finish. Only if I don't get to the canteen before eleven, I'll miss my supper. So' – he hesitated – 'can I go at five-to?'

'Bloody hell! What a skive!' sneered Furzer.

Speechless, the sergeant minutely studied the chits, his face reddening.

'Let me get this straight, Ryan. You have done sweet FA this evening and you are now asking me to release you early from the shift so you can stuff your guts and then sod off for a week-end's skive?'

'No, it's not a skive, Sarge. It's training. A weekend's training on my bike in the Peak District to improve my climbing ability. I compete in races for the station cycling team.'

'Training!' guffawed Furzer. 'In the Peak District? He lives there near enough, in Sheffield. He's off home for a friggin skive, that's what it is.'

But a fresh thought had penetrated the sergeant's wrath, transforming it to wonder. It was the concept of 'cycling'. Now he engaged Michael as if with a new species of animal and a tone of grudging respect entered his voice.

'Did you say cycling, Ryan? Biking? Pedal pushing? We are here in the middle of January. Out there it's dark as pitch and cold enough to freeze the goolies off a mummified camel and – am I right – you are proposing to go for a bloody bike ride?'

Michael nodded.

'Told you he was a nutter,' Furzer said.

But Worthington was lost in admiration. 'Let me get this absolutely straight,' he said. 'In the small hours of the sodding night, you are off pedalling up and down the leftovers of the Ice Age while everybody else is tucked up cosy and warm in his wanker?' He paused for reflection, still struggling to comprehend the enormity of this proposition. 'And you're not getting paid for this, Ryan? Nobody's forcing you? It's an act of – wotsit – free will?' Michael nodded again.

'Well bugger me if that doesn't take the biscuit. Here' – he returned the chits – 'take these, Gungadin, and piss off quick before I change my mind.'

'Good on yer, Sarge.' Giving Fuzzy the old two fingers, Michael was through the door in a flash and sprinting for the canteen. It was two minutes to eleven.

A brawny, tattooed arm was already on the shutter as he dashed up to the hatch and presented his chit. 'Kowalski!' sniffed the orderly. 'You'll have to take what's left.'

What was left consisted of a rubbery fried egg on a rasher of bacon in a pool of congealed fat, to which was added a slosh of beans, two slices of pappy bread, a knob of something yellowish and a spoonful of jam, all on the same cold platter. There was also a mug of stewed tea. Michael sat alone under the insomniac-sparrow-cheeping rafters and wolfed it all down, then made off to the billet.

Crossing the parade ground, he could see the dim outline of huts on the windswept, northern slope of the camp. Lights out had been 10.30 and they were all silent and dark, with one exception, his billet, number 22 on the hillcrest. Light leaked from behind tattered curtains and through its thin timber walls came the sound of an accordion. It was a Jimmy Shand Scottish reel. Duty sergeant gone blind and deaf, he thought? Wonder why? Opening the billet door and stepping into a warm fug of cigarette smoke, coke fumes and stale sweat, the reason became evident. A card school was at play on the floor beside the glowing stove. At the far end, Jock and Ewan were cavorting like drunken apes to the skirl from a wind up gramophone. Between times, as they twisted and turned, they hurled their cook's kitchen knives with splintering thuds into a target chalked on the broom-cupboard door.

Just his luck! The Gorbals Twins! No one tangled willingly with these unrelated so-called 'Twins' from the Glasgow slums, the joke being the only consanguinity they shared was their victims' blood. They were twinned in casual violence. Their fearsome reputation, not to mention underworld connections, was such that even a duty sergeant might turn the blind eye. But why weren't they still at work cleaning up the cookhouse – midnight was their time to come off shift and start raising hell? He began to feel queasy, the greasy supper rising in his throat.

Skirting round the card school, he sidled up to his bed space, cursing the fate that had billeted him with these tartan nutcases. He discarded his uniform and began pulling on his cycling togs, when his mate Alan rolled his head from under a pillow on the adjoining bed. 'Bloody hell! You're not off biking at this hour?'

''Fraid so. I'm off home. I've got a 48-hour pass. How long have Jock 'n' Ewan been on the loose?'

'Too bloody long! They've been on the hard stuff all night. They're pissed as newts. They were supposed to be on late shift, but they swapped last minute. Why, what's up?'

'What's up? My bike's in the broom-cupboard, that's all!'

To emphasise his point, there was another crash as Ewan's eight-inch blade slammed into the cupboard door.

'I left it there before shift, ready for a quick getaway.'

Alan sat up. 'If they've had their hands on it, I'd take my clothes off now and get into bed. You'll not be biking anywhere tonight!'

It was true, if they'd discovered his bike, it might now be a tangled wreck, the new sprint wheels booted square, the D'Allesandro tubular tyres cut to shreds. If the Twins could vent their spite on fellow human beings, they wouldn't hold back on a mere machine. He shuddered at the thought.

'I've got to see inside that broom cupboard, Alan.'

'You've gotta be jokin'! They're pissed outa their heads. They'll have you for target practice!'

Michael wondered how his hero Coppi would deal with this crisis – but then he had friends in the Mafia.

As he slipped on his cycling shoes, howls of glee drew his attention back to the Twins. The sleeping airman beside the broom-cupboard had had enough. He leapt barefoot out of bed and, clutching a blanket, tottered to join the card school at the stove. A foot above his pillow, a knife quivered in the wall. It must have been Jock's knife thrown blind backwards over his shoulder because now Ewan was repeating the trick. When he too missed the door and his blade ricocheted off the iron bed frame, the two men whooped and fell into a tripping embrace. As Michael watched, they play wrestled on the floor.

It was now or never, he decided. At least both knives were temporarily out of action. A few rapid strides took him to the cupboard. He opened it and there, to his joy, amongst the buckets and mops, rested his beautiful bike just as he'd left it, saddlebag packed and ready to go.

He'd barely time to experience relief. The wild laughter stopped and he sensed a presence breathing rank whisky fumes into the back of his neck. Hands on the bike, he turned round to look straight into the unrelenting, green eyes of Jock, head cocked in challenge, the snarling pocked snout of a crocodile.

'Who give yer leave t'open yon target door, ya glechit bastard?' The lips curled contemptuously. He became aware of a tremor running the length of his spine as he groped for an answer.

'I was – was –.' Then his eyes fell on the empty scotch bottle on Ewan's bed. 'It was an errand,' he stammered, aware of how stupid this sounded at a half before midnight, 'on my bike. I was just going down town to a late-night off-licence.'

Jock grabbed him by the collar. 'Y' hear that, Ewan? This man says he's goin' errand. Does he have our leave?'

Ewan was on his feet, staggering to retrieve his blade. 'He's a piece o' shit! He's goin' nowhere.'

Jock's grip tightened. 'Y' hear?' Michael was jerked close to the twisted mouth. 'We dinna like you, Ryan, Ewan 'n' me. You're a queer boy wi' them fancy togs 'n' that weird show-off bike o' yours. Y' think yer somethin'. Y' think yer a hard mon, no?'

'Aye,' said Ewan, 'he thinks he's hard ridin' his fasty-fasty bike, but he's a piece o' frit shit. An' y' know the worst? He's a mon never enjoys hisself.'

'Aye!' Jock was shaking him to and fro like a stopped clock. 'Y' never have any entertainment, y' glechit bastard!'

Their alcohol-slurred speech reinforced the threat. By

entertainment, Michael assumed they didn't mean cycling. They meant drinking, gambling, beating people up, whatever the criminal element enjoyed. He began a stuttering denial, but Jock shook him to silence as Ewan spoke again.

'D' y' fancy our entertainment, Ryan?' The knife blade flashed as he pointed and jabbed in emphasis. 'Cuttin'! We like cuttin' pieces o' show-off shit. Eh, Jock?'

'Right, Ewan!'

Michael had to believe it was the whisky talking and they were just showing off. But this was hardly the time to put his theory to the test. His constricted throat fished for calming words of reason. 'This errand, it's for Flight Lieutenant Kowalski,' he gasped, 'something he can't get in the officers' mess.'

At the mention of Kowalski, Jock's shaking touched a new level of menace. 'That's yon Polish wanker that meks a misery o' our lives wi his chits! Woz he wantin'?'

'Vodka.' Michael improvised desperately. 'Polish vodka.'

'Y' lyin' turd! There's nae sich thing. Vodka's Russian.'

Jock's fist was drawn back to prove his point on Michael's face when Ewan intervened. 'O aye, there is so, Jock. A good sup is Polish vodka.'

'How'd ye know that? Y' never drinked vodka in y' life!' snapped Jock, not to be denied.

'No?' Ewan insisted. 'No? Well that's you wrong. Y' remember the bar in Kelvinside we busted up 'n' me nuttin' the barman 'n' baggin's takings? He had a wee little bottle on the shelf, one o' they miniatures, 'n' ah tekkit 'n' ah give yer a drink of it.' Ewan was nodding triumphantly. 'Y' remember? Polish vodka!'

Michael was suddenly rocked back on his heels as Jock released his grip.

'Tha' was no vodka, y' loon. Tha' was schnaps!'

'Ye callin' _me_ loon? Loon y' sel'! Y' like a elephant wi no memory. Schnaps my arse! Ah read the label. Polish vodka.'

Jock was scornful. 'Read? When did ye learn readin'? Y' canno read y' own name!'

For some reason this slur sent Ewan wild. He threw his knife down and it landed quivering at Jock's feet. There followed a stream of oaths as the two intoxicated thugs locked horns in a finger-jabbing exchange.

Temporarily forgotten, Michael seized his opportunity and with his bike in tow, tiptoed away, passing beds with startled occupants risen like swaddled mummies from their pretend sleep, past the entranced gamblers, card hands mid-air, and out through the door. In the confusion his exit went unnoticed.

Outside, donning gloves, he became aware of his shaking hands and racing heart. Once astride the bike and freewheeling downhill to liberty in the damp night air, he wanted to shout aloud with relief. It was cycling made life on camp bearable. Without its small excitements to offset the boring routine, petty restrictions and the billet's bullying, he didn't know what he'd do – though he supposed he'd manage somehow, like everyone else, counting the days down to demob.

He left his lights switched off. The last thing he desired was to advertise his presence to the guardhouse and suffer more delay. He needn't have worried. The window was steamed up and closed as he slipped under the barrier and out onto the public highway.

With the tawny neon glow of the town at his back, he tightened his toe-straps and danced up Sandon hill. His eyes quickly adjusted to the darkness, picking out the pale road unrolling ahead. At this late hour traffic would be negligible. Saving his batteries for the misty Derbyshire moors seemed like a good idea.

On the Uttoxeter road he found himself pedalling into a northerly breeze that chilled his hands, even through the gloves. Far and away a church clock chimed midnight. With sixty hilly miles to cover, he planned to be home by 4.00 a.m. Home, a brief welcome break from the harsh, masculine world of military service – a good meal, hot bath and long sleep in his own soft bed. Mum, pre-warned by letter, was expecting him, attentive for the pre-dawn tap on the door. It would be the same old greeting. 'Did you have a nice ride?' As if cycling was ever just 'nice'! Good old Mum!

Later, near Mayfield, on the undulating road to Ashbourne, he briefly switched on his front lamp as a car laboured towards him uphill, its milky beams parting the trees and forcing him to screw up his eyes – an old pre-war banger, as it turned out, probably some doctor or other essential service on late night call.

One day I'll own a car, he mused, crouching low on the bars, the wind whipping his hair as he dropped into the valley. No banger though – something special for a cycling ace. A Rolls or a Bentley or one of those big American Buicks from the movies, all chrome bumpers and white-wall tyres. People will stare and say, 'There goes Michael Ryan! He's a big-time cycling pro. He's got this huge house on the Riviera. Servants. The lot.'

Such meditation shortened the miles until he crossed the Dove, rushing in winter flood, and cycled through Ashbourne's silent streets – just visible the clock on its high steeple, palely luminous, the hands indicating one–thirty. He was making decent time despite the headwind. Nevertheless he rose from the saddle to attack the hill out of town and was half way up when something brought him to a gasping halt.

A shape floated from a doorway, like a gigantic black bat. It barred his way, passing a light from wing to wing signalling him to stop. Then it advanced and became a uniformed constable in a cape bearing a torch. The powerful beam almost blinded him. He dismounted.

'Now then, young man,' the constable began, 'I thought I saw you coming but couldn't be sure as you had no front light and' – pausing to circle the bike – 'no rear light neither, it would seem, which is contrary to the law. You are aware it's an offence to ride an un-illuminated pedal cycle during the hours of darkness?' He adopted an erect, official pose 'You could've rid me down and both of us ended up in hospital.'

Given he was climbing a 1-in-6 hill very slowly, this claim seemed somewhat exaggerated, but Michael chose the path of discretion. 'Sorry, officer. I had to stop for a call of nature a mile back. Turned the lights off to save the batteries and clean forgot to turn them on again.'

It was a lame excuse and he knew it. The policeman hummed sceptically. 'I might ask where you're going at' – consulting his pocket watch – 'one-thirty three of a winter's morning. More to the point, I might ask where you've come from?' He was looking with forensic interest at Michael's bulky saddlebag.

'I'm doing my national service. I've come from camp and I'm going home. To Sheffield. I've got a weekend pass.' He produced it and the constable shone his torch on the crumpled paper.

'One o' the Brylcreem boys, eh?' he said, softening. 'And this Kow what's-his-name, your officer, what's he, Polish?'

Michael, cold and eager to be away, nodded.

Returning the chit, the constable adopted an avuncular tone. 'Well now, as an ex-serviceman myself, I'm well acquainted with the attractions of home. No place like it, as they say. So on this occasion I'll not detain you further. Everything seems to be in order. Now switch on them lights and keep 'em on.' He stood aside.

Michael made to remount his bike when a heavy, gloved hand fell on his shoulder.

'Just another word in your shell-like.' The tone was confidential. 'We're on red alert tonight. There's a dangerous man out there on the loose. Be in all tomorrow's papers. Escaped from Rampton High Security for the criminally insane and they say he's probably headed for Sheffield where his mother lives. He's nicked a sports cycle from somebody's shed. So keep your eyes peeled. There may be a roadblock in Bakewell or up beyond on the moors. They'll want to get him back inside before he causes any more grief.'

'What's he done?'

'Ex-special services commando, hears voices. God ordered him to strangle his missus, her mother and their pet black cat.' The constable laughed. 'First two you might understand – but that poor moggy! He called it Satan and twisted its neck – well, no wonder they sent him to the loony bin instead of to the gallows!'

With a cheery salute, the constable dispatched him.

At the crest of the hill, he stopped again to don his spare zip-up windcheater and the balaclava helmet from a saddlebag pocket. The night was icy and his temples throbbed from the raw wind. Now he took comfort from the balaclava with only his nose and eyes exposed. But despite covering up, akin to ducking under the sheets in a haunted bedroom, there was no hiding from the constable's dire warning and a far more fearful sort of exposure.

Now, if anything, the darkness seemed to intensify. One friendly town lay behind, the next far ahead. In between was nothing but black solitude, the emptiness of the Peak. Navigating a lonesome path, he clung to the trail his lamp illuminated – broken white lines and winking Catseyes.

But he was no longer alone. The constable had provided company. Let loose inside his head was a crazed killer so violent, the Twins seemed like cherubs. What if he was lying in wait, crouched invisible in a ditch, a coiled spring of lunatic rage alerted by the approaching telltale light of a cycle lamp?

It was an unlikely scenario, he admitted, but so was the Twins' unexpected appearance in the billet. Strange things happened and life was unpredictable. He could still feel the imprint of Jock's hands close to his throat, as if it had been a sort of rehearsal. The thought was terrifying. To shake himself free, he sprinted two hundred yards flat out in top gear. Then he gave up. Better proceed with caution, he reasoned, and keep his eyes skinned, than blind into the killer's trap.

The sudden adrenalin flow did him no favour, but instead sharpened his senses to the reality around him. Those shadowy shapes high up on the ridge? The stirrings and half-stifled groans floating off the fields? Trees? Beasts? Or something much more sinister? A shiver ran down his spine. Hereabouts in the Peak was a haunted history of stone circles and ancient burial grounds, ritual sacrifices, ghosts, monsters and ghouls. The boggarts of Arbor Low. The phantom servant at the Olde Gate Inn. The headless travellers. All easy to laugh off by light of day. Foolish superstition! But now, in this lonesome cavern of a moonless winter's night, he couldn't be sure of what lay at either hand, or ahead or worse, behind.

For now, adding to the soft swish of his tyres and whirr of his Simplex derailleur, came another sound, unearthly in its insistence. There it was again, louder now. Something was following him. As he accelerated, so did the sound, pursuing him remorselessly up the long, winding ascent of Longcliffe, down to the Via Gellia, up to the Miner's Standard and down the twisting descent past the Hermit's Cave, Robin Hood's crag and the Nine Stones where the Grey Ladies danced. It was unmistakeably another bicycle, sometimes distant, sometimes so close he felt he'd only to turn to confront his pursuer face to face. That is, if the thing had a face…

He dared not look back, but in a sweat of fear, settled low on the drops and wound the pedals harder and harder past the dim outline of battlemented Haddon Hall until finally, with relief, he reached the town of Bakewell. There, under a solitary street lamp marking the right turn to Sheffield, he stopped and looked back. The road was deserted. But dismounting, he discovered a twig jammed between mudguard and wheel, a tiny stick of hawthorn rubbing at the tyre. What an idiot he'd been! He swallowed hard. Like a school kid, he'd let his imagination run riot. He really had to get a grip.

He was through the town before he recalled the constable in Ashbourne. There'd been no roadblock, not even a copper skulking in a doorway. Good! Maybe the strangler had been caught and everyone stood down and returned to base?

It was 3.00 a.m. and it had been a long tough ride into the freezing headwind, yet he still felt strangely alert and alive. He was on familiar territory. Another hour of steady cycling lay ahead – the run down Thirteen Bends to Chatsworth Park and Baslow village, then the slog up Baslow Hill to the Peacock Inn on the moors overlooking Sheffield. There he would observe the city's twinkling street lights, an amber and white galaxy, stretching and curling away below into the misty distance and journey's end.

On the hill he chattered the derailleur onto the bottom sprocket. Then it was a case of sitting back in the saddle and pedalling, sliding the bike up the long gradient through a funnel of grit-stone boulders and cliffs.

He was over half way when he heard a car engine droning behind. It would be the first vehicle he'd encountered since Ashbourne. A headlight picked him out and threw his shadow in a sharpening arc onto the tarmac. It approached, slowed and finally passed, a big Humber, with the outlines of men inside staring stonily ahead. Then it was gone, its tail lights swallowed in the gloom.

As he reached the open moor, he saw the car again. It was parked in a small lay-by facing towards him, lights extinguished, and behind it a second identical vehicle. Both shadowy cars appeared empty, but as he neared he heard an engine ticking as it cooled. Where were the occupants?

Next moment he found out as all hell broke loose. Whistles blew, and at the signal, figures clambered from behind the bordering stone walls and bore down, screeching commands for him to stop. He was half blinded by the sudden intrusion of headlights. He halted and put a foot to the road, but had no chance to dismount. A blow from behind smashed him down on top of his bike. 'Grab his hands!' someone shouted, and his arms were pinioned behind his back and he felt the pinch of cold steel at his wrists. Someone smelling strongly of tobacco had him by the throat and was squeezing. Panic struck home. He couldn't breathe or speak.

'Now then, George, don't give us any trouble and we won't have to hurt you,' said the voice close to his ear. 'Get him up on his feet!' The pressure was released.

He was dragged up and extricated from the bike.

'That's right, nice and easy does it, George, and you'll be back in your cosy little cell sipping your Horlicks before you know it. Remove that mask, Jackson.'

He winced with pain as strands of his hair were ripped off with the balaclava.

There was a long silence.

As his eyes adjusted to the glare, he took in the scene. He was surrounded by at least eight burly men, some in police uniform bearing truncheons. They were contemplating him with a mixture of dismay and disgust. Then one of the younger constables said, smirking, 'This ain't him, Sir.'

'I can see that for myself, Rutter,' snapped a tall plain-clothes officer in a white Gannex mac. He wore a tartan scarf and a trilby was tipped back on his head revealing a smart, grey parting. 'So what the hell is he doing up here on a racer bike at this godforsaken hour? Check his pockets – and check that saddlebag.'

First they found his racing licence, zipped into a top pocket. Big Gannex read aloud from it by torchlight, slowly as if the words were foreign. 'British League of Racing Cyclists. Third category. Michael Ryan.' He squinted at the photograph, sharing it with another plain-clothes man.

'Anything in that bag, Rutter?'

'A load o' jumble mainly, Sir, and these funny looking inner-tubes.' He held a pair of D'Allessandro tubular tyres up for inspection.

'So,' said Gannex, 'budding Reg 'Arris, are we?' Then he was handed the crumpled, sweat-damp leave-pass and he stiffened angrily.

'Why the bloody hell didn't you say you was a serviceman straight out, instead of wasting our time?'

'You never give me a chance,' shouted Michael, fighting back the tears. 'You just knocked me flying. I've hurt my knee and you've probably half wrecked my bike.'

'Rutter! Check that machine.'

Rutter snapped to attention and ran to pick up the bike.

'What's he know?' said Michael.

'A darned sight more than you,' said Gannex. 'He rides a bike every day of his life – on his beat. Well, Rutter?'

The expert cycle mechanic spun the front wheel, tried the brake and waggled the handlebars. 'It's in perfect working order, Sir,' he reported. 'A bit flimsy though.'

'It's a lightweight,' Michael protested. 'It fell down on its alloy crank. That's probably bent now. Pedal spindle too. Ruined.'

Rutter looked aggrieved. 'If my crank was bent, I'd take a big hammer to it. Simple as that, Sir.'

'There you are,' said Gannex. 'You heard what the constable said. Problem solved.' He looked grim-faced. 'Any more complaints, Michael Ryan?'

'Yes. If this is supposed to be a free country, why am I still in handcuffs?'

At a nod the cuffs were removed and Michael began rubbing the circulation back into his wrists.

'Look at it from our point of view,' Gannex urged. 'We're hunting a very dangerous man. Ex-commando, trained killer. What's more this gentleman hears voices inside his head. God tells him to do things to people. Nasty things. Our info is that he has escaped from Rampton, having half strangled one of the warders there, has nicked a racer bike and is on his way home to Sheffield to see his mum, probably to strangle her if he gets the order from on high. So, do you understand, son? You happen along, on a racer bike, with your face covered, same height, same strong build, heading towards Sheffield, in the middle of the night. Bang! You fit the bill and we pounce. And it's just your bad luck.'

'All right,' Michael said, 'all right. So you've made a mistake. You knock a perfectly innocent person to the ground. You injure him and you damage his bike, an expensive bike he's had to save up for ages to buy. You treat him like a criminal and you don't even say sorry...'

'Sorry?' Big Gannex cut him short. 'You're wanting sympathy? *Our* sympathy?' He looked round the group for support. 'Watson, you see someone on a bike out on the moors in the middle of the night and it's mid-winter – what do you think?'

'A bit weird?' suggested Watson.

'My thoughts exactly. A bit weird!' He fixed Michael with another piercing glare. 'And people who do weird things and come unstuck don't deserve sympathy.'

'It's a free country,' Michael insisted.

'It's only a free country if you're a normal person. If you're like George and have a penchant for strangling people, it's not a free country. And if you're a bit weird' – he wagged a fat finger under Michael's nose – 'it's only a bit free.' He turned to Rutter, who was still smirking. 'Give him a cup of coffee.'

'Out o' *my* flask, Sir?" Rutter was aghast.

'Stuff your coffee!' said Michael. 'Stuff it!'

The group stirred at this ingratitude.

'You've had a bit of bad luck,' said Inspector Gannex menacingly. 'Don't make it worse. We could have you for wasting police time. We could have you for riding a bike with lights like red hot hatpins. We could find things in your saddlebag you didn't know you had. We could run you down the station, put you in a cell and throw away the key for the weekend. Then we could phone up your Commanding Officer for a character reference. Wouldn't he be pleased? No more weekend passes for you. So don't chance your luck with us, son.'

He held out the chit and racing licence and, as Michael reached his hand out, let them drop on the road. 'Third class,' he sneered. 'Is that the best you can do, Reg?'

He turned on his heel and headed back to the car, the others trooping after him. 'We'll check at Fox House. See if they've had any joy over there.'

Michael stuffed the documents back into his pocket and picked up his bike. One car turned and headed off. He stood shivering in the icy wind as its tail lights disappeared into the murk.

* * * *

'Is something wrong, love?'

'No.'

'Only you're looking right pinched.' His Mum in her dressing gown is tidying away the breakfast things. 'Are they feeding you properly?'

'Not bad.'

She eyes him suspiciously. 'Something is wrong. I've not been your mum all these years for nothing. I can tell when things aren't right. Your hands are shaking. You haven't had to do jankers again?'

'Course not!'

'Can I ask why you're limping?'

He shakes his head and gulps at the hot, sweet tea. 'It's nothing. Banged my knee at work, that's all. And I'm still a bit cold.'

'Well, happen you'll tell me tomorrow when you're rested. Just remember, if there's anything your dad and me can do to help –'

She goes upstairs to run his bath.

Afterwards, he lies in bed, unable to sleep, his swollen knee throbbing and Gannex's taunt ringing in his ears. An hour passes. Two. Dawn breaks through the curtains, casting a grey light over the room. He hears the old, familiar, civilised sound of the milkman's electric float and bottles rattling at the front door, but nothing comforts him. It seems like a world of bullying injustice and no one can help, not his parents, not Kowalski, not even his friends, except to offer sympathy. The wind whistling down the chimney is from the north and will blow him back to camp. There he must face the music. Grovel to the Twins. Fork out a bribe of booze and fags from his meagre pay packet. Now he's on their radar there's no escape.

He cuddles the hot water bottle, willing himself to sleep. He remembers some advice Alan once gave. 'Don't count sheep. Count the days to demob. Count down the days, mate, until you walk out past that guardroom, a free man.'

He calculates four hundred and fifty-six days left to serve. An eternity! He closes his eyes and begins counting. At somewhere beyond a hundred and fifty, the numbers take on human shape. He is at the roadside on top of some great col, counting the riders over the summit. A hundred and seventy. Two hundred. It must be some big professional race. Two hundred and twenty-five. One by one they appear in a long, never-ending chain snaking back down the mountainside. He counts them as they pass. Three hundred. Three hundred and fifty. There are so many of them. And still they come, all the professional racing cyclists in the world. He is the counter and they the counted. He stands outside the tinted page on which they pass, yearning to be amongst them, but he remains a spectator and nothing more as mist falls on the mountaintop and sleep takes him up in its merciful arms.

FIRST RACE, FIRST CLUB

As a kid and into my teens I was an unadulterated ball games fanatic. From marbles to football, cricket to basketball, table tennis, snooker – the spherical absorbed my attention and became a cornerstone of my existence. But then, out of the blue, came that life changing adventure with the Fabulous Elsecar Cycling Club and my fancy took a sideward drift. It didn't happen all at once. It was as if a seed was planted in my mind waiting to be fertilised. And out of that would grow an alternative pastime that required an entirely different sort of balls.

My elder brother John, a member of Sheffield Central CC, and his fiancée Marjorie, to spend more private time together, began sharing a tandem at weekends. One Sunday, being at a loose end, I was invited to join them on one of their jaunts into the Derbyshire and Nottinghamshire countryside and then in subsequent weeks, as I seemed to be enjoying myself and persisting, we pedalled further afield on the odd weekend youth hostel trip to the cathedral cities of York, Chester and Lincoln. Now, with hindsight, I can see their motives were mixed and it was not simply a case of charitably entertaining a gawky teenager with little else to do. Courtship amongst Catholic folk in that straight laced era was a very formal affair, and I can well imagine my presence as quasi-chaperon served to reassure the two families concerned that the chances of unlicensed high jinx or hanky-panky would be limited prior to the walk to the altar.

It wasn't easy. I took some terrible beatings on those first few long rides, though perversely the more I suffered the more I seemed to look forward to challenging and overcoming the torment of the next weekend. On my cross-eyed, cripple of a Dunelt sports bike, it was like dragging a heavy sack of coal on the road behind me. Without preparation I had jumped from riding 10 miles per day to 60 and 70 and I suffered horrendously from hunger knock, sometimes dismounting so weak-kneed on reaching the tea place that I could barely stand. My extreme pallor gave cause for concern. 'Are you all right?' I was repeatedly asked. 'I'm fine thanks, just need a cuppa.' I was only fourteen, beset with all the usual adolescent qualms concerning nascent manliness and unwilling to admit to weakness. I would rather die than be thought of as a 'cissy'.

Several weeks of these near death experiences so impressed my brother with my perseverance that he donated his Langsett track frame and built me up a new bike around it. 'I don't suppose I'll be needing this again,' he said wistfully, thinking perhaps of the marital burden he was about to assume. 'My racing days are over.'

So I took on the trappings of a proper cyclist. The short-wheelbase Langsett was everything the Dunelt wasn't: light, lively, responsive and perfectly in track, a handbuilt example of the frame builder's art. It was beautiful to behold, being painted in a lovely burgundy shade of red; its baroque extravaganza of hand-filed curlicue lugs would have charmed a Victorian cabinet-maker. The effect on me was instantaneous and liberating. The thought of riding 70 miles no longer terrified, and I easily outpaced the tandem on the hills. I was stretching my wings and it was time for me to go it alone.

One winter Sunday the tandem pair had to be home early for an evening engagement and I asked if I could stay out for tea on my own. My mum and dad needed reassurance that I was grown up and savvy enough not to get lost in the dark or fall off under a lorry, but at length they agreed. I remember that huge feeling of excitement as after lunch I launched off with only myself for company. For the first time in my life I would be out after dark far from home, alone and totally in charge of my own destiny.

It was the 1940s and the countryside in general and Peak District in particular were much more remote and cut-off from urban civilisation than they are nowadays in the age of car ownership and the mobile phone. Neither my brother nor parents had a landline phone or motorcar, so if I got into difficulties I would have to rescue myself as best I could, becoming my own navigator and bicycle repairman and exercising something called common sense, then the agreed solution to every problem under the sun. 'Use your common sense, lad,' was the cry. I just couldn't wait to take this enormous step towards adulthood and personal freedom.

There was then a magical little Derbyshire café, close to the hamlet of Birchover, that was popular with hikers and cyclists in the know, and there I had in mind to mark this rite of passage by eating mum's homemade potted meat sandwiches alongside of a sixpenny pot of tea. Café is far too grand a title for this hillside Lilliputian, two up and down stone cottage, abode of amiable old Mrs Oxley, who had retired here from a nursing post in Stourbridge. Her wee parlour doubled up as the tearoom. But what it lacked in modern amenities was more than compensated for by the prize of quaintness: its Jacobean doll's house interior with stout, time-blackened beams, the log fire and sooty, long-spouted tinker's kettle, like an anarchist's bomb steaming on the hob; Buster, the black cat, purring soporifically in the hearth, the soothing scent of wood smoke, the shoeplate-clacking flagstones. Even her brackish tasting tea grew on you in the knowledge that the water had come from an adjacent granite trough fed by a stream off the rabbit-run hill – oh, such life giving freshness! And oh, the romance! It was the very epitome of a bucolic tea place such as now exists only in Frank Paterson's charming sketches of a long-lost, pre-war England.

I presented myself on Mrs Oxley's stone doorstep, hollowed by centuries of comings and goings, and knocked. What passed through her mind on confronting a flushed fourteen-year old boy in the four o'clock dusk, I cannot imagine. She was a fervent spiritualist and claimed Cardinal Richlieu as her spirit guide, so was already no doubt acquainted with apparitions from the Other Side. (Four centuries previously, such eccentricity might have got her burned as a witch). I was her only customer and sat down at a rickety table, munching my sandwiches in silence. The clock ticked, the fire crackled and spat and Buster retreated under a chair. As time passed and nothing was said, I began to feel increasingly affronted by her lack of curiosity – surely, one so young arriving late, alone and so unexpectedly, wasn't I a wunderkind worthy of some remark or question? To stimulate conversation, I mentioned that en route to her front door I had paused to stand inside the twilit stone circle at nearby Stanton in Peak, in the hope a procession of Druids might emerge from out of the trees. That was true and I had stood inside the circle and wondered about the people who must once have worshipped there. But if it was intended as a gesture to her spiritualism and to impress her with my grown-up sophistication, it failed to provoke a response. From her fireside rocking chair, she peered at me over her spectacles with a rather strange regard and said nothing.

This was England, 1948. The economy was exhausted from the war effort, the nation broke and almost everything rationed. Even Mrs Oxley's home-baked scones lacked proper dried fruit – she made do with bilberries culled from the hillside. In his recent book *Austerity Britain*, author David Kynaston gives us a taste of what it was to live at this time of deprivation:

No supermarkets, no motorways, no teabags, no sliced bread, no frozen food – no dishwashers, no mobiles, no duvets, no Pill. Abortion illegal, homosexual relationships illegal, suicide illegal, capital punishment legal – televisions almost unknown – no 'teenagers'. Heavy coins, heavy shoes, heavy suitcases, heavy tweed coats, heavy leather footballs, no unbearable lightness of being. Meat rationed, butter rationed, lard rationed, margarine rationed, sugar rationed, tea rationed, cheese rationed, jam rationed, eggs rationed, sweets rationed, soap rationed, clothes rationed. Make do and mend.

Post-war youngsters like me grew up without any of the material benefits today's teenagers take for granted. But unlike the legion of minor celebrities now cashing in on their childhood misery memoirs, we never felt deprived, for we had known nothing else. The gap between rich and poor was narrower than now and everyone except a small, London-based elite was in the same boat. We lived for the day. Repeated studies have shown that on our meagre diets we were healthier, happier and less angst ridden than present-day, much wealthier generations. Above all, we were not cosseted by risk-averse parents, but allowed the freedom to roam and, from practical personal experience, learn to cope with danger. Life was enriched by self-created excitement that owed little or nothing to wealth or social class.

So, though I must have lived in an age of make-do-and-mend deprivation, to me at the time it was normality. And outside and above this normality on that dark winter's night was the seventh heaven of sitting astride my beautiful, burgundy bicycle and making a triumphal progress homewards, the happiest, most fulfilled boy on earth.

Having gained my badge of independence, I was ambitious to voyage farther and faster and began to cycle more often with my peers. Doug, a lad from the council estate, now became my Sunday companion. He was my physical antithesis. Where I was thin, undeveloped and plagued by bronchial problems, he was robustly healthy and broad shouldered, with muscles to tear a tank in half. He was our cricket team's demon bowler, terrifying the opposition with his tireless ability to hurl the ball at speed, with lift and unpredictability, and many a batsman 'retired hurt' rather than continue to face his merciless onslaught. With the bat he was usually good for a few sixes once his eye was in. Accompanying this physical prowess went a pleasant easy-going personality, not showy or boastful, a combination I found attractive. It meant we could race each other up hills without it becoming a grudge match, and he was a measure by which I could test my own strength and stamina without ever feeling demeaned if they didn't match up. He was never triumphal: nothing more than a playful grin marked his victories over me and he accepted his rare defeats with good grace and some such comment as, 'Your mum been feedin' you up with Virol?'[Virol: a bone marrow preparation for children and invalids.]

As the months went by and we churned out the Sunday miles exploring the lanes of Derbyshire, Nottinghamshire, South Yorkshire and Lincolnshire, I began to get his measure. I won my fair share of the half-wheeling duels and uphill sprints to which the beautiful countryside was merely an unacknowledged backdrop. I don't think it was this establishment of parity that caused our friendship to draw to a close. Other things were afoot in his life. His interest in cycling was on the wane. Calling at his house to make arrangements, I would find him increasingly vague. It was 'maybe – perhaps – I'll have to see what I'm doing'. He had left school and was apprenticed to a carpenter. He had less free time and was mixing more in the adult world. He never let on, but perhaps he had a girl friend. At any rate, it seemed his other engagements were more pressing than our cycling excursions and, reading the signals, I let him go his own way.

I write here of Doug in some detail, not just because he was a milestone in my cycling career, but also because he perfectly illustrates my 'a dog is not just for Xmas' theory. Cycling can be simply utilitarian or a lifelong spiritual experience akin to religion. There are those who cycle and those who have cycling in their blood. For the former, like Doug, it fulfils a temporary need; for the latter it represents a constant itch that demands to be scratched.

I turned to other companions from the estate and school. Our rides together tended to be short, after school 'blinds', sprinting the hills and for '30' signs, or in the holidays half-wheeling marathons of 80 to100 miles. That summer my lifelong friend Tom Mayfield and I passed the super distance, 150 miles challenge of Sheffield to Cleethorpes and back. Reaching the seaside resort beloved of northern plebeians, we made for the beach, the farthest point from home, and sat on the sands to eat our sandwiches, staring dumbly out at the choppy, seal-grey North Sea. It was a breezy July lunchtime, with squawking gulls fighting over discarded chip wrappers whilst exhausted parents, sheltering behind windbreaks, and their squabbling kids gave a passable impression of enjoyment. Having marked our cards with a gritty ice-cream cornet apiece, we set off back home. I remember nearing Rotherham at 140 miles and asserting my dominance over a trolleybus by outsprinting it as it pulled away sharply from the kerbside. The driver was outraged as I squeezed past him on the outside.

We were both fifteen years old and on our diet of deprivation fit as fleas. I find it hard to believe that any of today's indulged yet 'bored' teenagers could match us for energy or, indeed, zest for life.

Eventually all of us would join clubs and race. I was influenced in my choice by something that took place during a bike ride with Johnnie, a dyed-in-the-wool RTTC clubman. One Sunday, when the tandem couple couldn't accompany me, I was entrusted to this war veteran's 'guidance'. We were climbing side by side up Moscar on the Sheffield–Glossop road when another cyclist suddenly came whirring past and, with no acknowledgement to our presence, pulled away. He was crouched low over a glittering racing machine with no mudguards. He wore black, tight-fitting shorts, white ankle socks and a colourful jersey, with food bulking his musette and a spare tubular encircling his shoulders. He was bronzed and, though the weather was overcast, wore dark sunglasses. I had seen photos of Fausto Coppi in *Cycling*, but here he was in person out on a training ride. And here we were, a couple of over-dressed 'saddlebags' plodding along. Obviously, he had more to do with his breath than say hello.

All of this infuriated Johnnie. 'Get in behind, kid, and hang on,' he said. I did as I was told and the pace stepped up. Despite Johnnie's best efforts though, 'Coppi' pulled relentlessly away and by the summit was out of sight. With a growl, Johnnie gave up. 'Ter-werring BLRC show-off,' he snarled, before asking if I was OK. I was breathing hard and feeling rather strangulated, but very proud as I had indeed 'hung on'.

I'd heard of the BLRC and now had some inkling why there was no love lost between them and the RTTC. But I had never before come across a League member in the rebel flesh and assumed they existed underground like secret resistance fighters. I was immensely impressed by this first encounter. Show off? Certainly not! More like show the way.

When I recounted this incident to my brother, I was taken aback when he showed no sympathy for Johnnie. 'My advice to you,' he said, 'is to join a League club. It's too late for me, but I'm convinced our future lies with Stallard. The other lot have no guts.'

For the time being though, my friends and I kept our options open. In the racing season there was a midweek evening 10 miles time trial on the so-called Wortley course north of the city, and we youngsters would turn out to gawp at the grown men performing on their stripped-down racing machines. The ceremony of signing on and warming up seemed easy enough and the formality of the occasion, contrasting starkly with our own disorganised 'blinds', seemed to offer us an alternative and more accurate way to measure ourselves against each other. Perhaps that was why, when the invitation came to 'have a go', we hesitated. The time trial is called the race of truth, but sometimes the truth can be unpalatable. Eventually, though, we talked ourselves into accepting, taking courage from each other.

We made no special preparations apart from removing mudguards. None of us had sprint wheels or 'genuine' racing garb, just ordinary linen touring shorts and tee shirts or thin sweaters. I had no idea how to ride a race. With my brother I had witnessed track meetings at Manchester's Fallowfield and thrilled as stars like Reg Harris and Arie Van Vliet strained every sinew over the final two hundred yards of a sprint match, charging heads down like buffaloes, before thrusting their machines over the line. I supposed this was how you should ride a time trial, flat out all the way.

It was a restricted gear event, 72 inches (e.g. 48x18). I set off twiddling like a hamster on acid and after a mile of *faux-plat* into a headwind was close to collapse. Without knowing it, I had raced myself into oxygen debt, and riders began to overtake, seemingly silky smooth and with low aerodynamic poise and economy of effort. One, two, three, four swept by at intervals, each a blow to my already sagging morale. My time was 29.54, just inside 'evens' and far slower than the unrealistic 26 I'd hoped for. Afterwards I squatted at the roadside, lungs on fire, coughing myself sick. So this was the race of truth. The crowning blow was to discover one of my companions had beaten me by a few seconds. It was not an experience I was in any hurry to repeat.

In the end we all joined League clubs. It was one thing to race ten miles on a warm summer's evening, quite another to rise with the lark and subject yourself to Sunday after Sunday of lonesome agony, just to see if you could better your previous time. It was pragmatism set us against the RTTC. We were repelled by the loneliness of the early morning time trial and could see no reason for it, not to mention having to wear that dour, Calvinistic, black racing garb and experience the creepy feeling of indulging in something 'underhand', quasi-illegal and 'shameful' that accorded with the paranoid attitude of the RTTC. We contrasted that with the 'real' cycle racing we read of in the continental magazines and increasingly observed first hand in the Derbyshire hills. The riders stood proud. The sport was open and for all to see. Our hearts were captured by the unashamed colour, vivacity and sheer joyousness of racing with the League.

I was the first to break ranks and join a club. The Sheffield Phoenix and Sheffield Racing Cycling Club were obvious choices. They had the most stars and the most race winners and if I'd wanted to be associated with stylish success, that was where to look. But I had other ideas and chose the Sheffield Mercury, after going out with them on a couple of trial rides. They competed regularly, but had no pushy stars and seemed less elitist, and I sensed there would be no pressure on me for early success. The membership was overwhelmingly youthful (the exception being self-styled coach Arnie, a male mother hen who patrolled up and down club runs lecturing us constantly on 'how to ride properly in a group and how to get fit' and whom we disparaged as 'The Old-Timer' – he was about 40). It covered a wide range of ability and there was a strong social side. The club runs were just that and not mini races, so I could fade into the background if I wished. Moreover, the membership boasted some rather pretty doe-eyed females of about my own age – an unexplored species for someone like myself, educated in the all boys environment of a Catholic grammar school.

The Mercury revolved around another 'old-timer' war veteran, secretary Bill Thompson, a moon-faced patriarch and later vice-chairman of the BLRC, who ran a small cycle shop in Chesterfield Road. There we congregated on Saturday afternoons, jostling for space with display hangers of cycles, tyres and wheels, spluttering over Bill's piping hot condensed milk tea, chatting, planning the next ride or race, inspecting the latest equipment and occasionally making a purchase. The need to force an entry to the counter through this cram jam-packed interior must have put off many a potential casual customer. In winter, condensation streamed in rivulets down the windows. But it was just this cheerful, paraffin heated fug of a self-enclosed world with its sense of intimate family belonging that attracted me. Moreover, Bill ran the most generous 'book' in the city, enabling low wage apprentices and hard-up school kids like myself to up-date their equipment by paying half a crown or five bob a week: effectively an interest-free hire purchase scheme run entirely on trust – no signed contract, just a scribbled note in Bill's grimy ledger and the verbal promise to pay. Surely, I thought, doing the maths, this must be a ballooning recipe for bankruptcy, especially since some people seemed to keep adding more and more to their credit? Apparently not, for despite some bad debts, on just such a shaky financial basis, many a small cycle shop like Bill's ticked on into the Sixties, when a downturn in the cycle trade forced them to the wall.

There was something of the trademark BLRC 'take the bull by the horns' about Bill, well illustrated by the following anecdote. About twelve months after I joined the club, I left school and entered the civil service. I was posted to a job in Leeds involving a daily four hours bus journey, which ate into my spare time and took the edge off my training and racing. On mentioning this to Bill, he immediately jumped into action. 'I'll find you a job in Sheffield,' he said, locking up the shop and telling me to follow him as he took to his bike. We ended up in a yard behind the local branch of his bank. He tapped on the back door and then, with no prior appointment, walked straight into the manager's office. There behind his desk sat the manager in smart suit, collar and tie, and here was Bill in his greasy old workshop togs, hair all awry, with scruffy me in tow. We must have looked a right pair. After a brief exchange of greetings, totally unabashed, Bill said, 'This young man's looking for a job and I can tell you he's highly qualified, aren't you, Tony?' He had sprung this on me with no forewarning and all I could do was nod. Bank managers were then pillars of the community, the very acme of bourgeois respectability, and this man must have been absolutely flabbergasted and not a little alarmed by this sudden backdoor intrusion into his inner sanctum. There was no interview. He simply spluttered words to the effect that he would see what he could do if a vacancy came up. Outside again, Bill gave me a wink as if to say problem solved. Of course, I heard nothing more about it and had no desire anyway to work in a bank.

Away from Bill's shop, the Mercury's official clubroom was situated in a warren of cobbled, sooty, back streets and alleys that a decade later would be demolished under the slum clearance programme, to make way for high-rise flats. There we met on Monday and Friday evenings. From a litter strewn, rat-run backyard you ascended shaky timber steps to a boarded room above a tumbledown workshop: think Fagin's Den. Any modern day Health and Safety official would have had apoplexy on sight of the ancient wiring and trip-trap lumps of hardboard tagged over holes in the floor. The only power source came from two dangling light sockets. A bulb would be removed so that a one bar electric fire, or alternatively a toaster, could be plugged in. Now and then the resulting overload caused the open fuse box to splutter and arc like a nanosecond Catherine Wheel. 'Put a bloody nail across it!' demanded one of the crazier members. Fortunately, no one ever did or the place might have gone up in smoke with all of us inside.

We lounged around in wrecked armchairs, sipping tea from stained, cracked, soapy tasting mugs. To young, ever hungry wanderers the burnt toast spread with margarine and jam or Bovril tasted wonderful. Much talk was of fitness gained and lost, plaintive excuses for "going off the back" in races and training rides, boasts of triumphs to come. Some loudmouths plainly lied like fishermen, stretching distance and squeezing time to make a heroic myth out of plain endeavour. The mascara-eyed girls, even prettier in the pale light, giggled in mocking disbelief.

'Awreight, kid?'

'Ay fine, thanks, Arnie.'

Thus I was acknowledged and accepted, though as a shy newcomer I thought it best to keep well in the background.

I used to love the club runs, especially when we stopped to pile into a café for tea. Musettes hooked over chair backs, the cross table banter would begin, with lots of joking and micky-taking to spurts of uproarious laughter. The summer pea and pie suppers were a delight. Afterwards, we rode home through the warm dusk, past cottages, before television's flickering advent, still lit by oil lamps. As often as not we would be singing. Someone might open up with a snatch from a current pop song – 'Shrimp Boats is a Comin'' or Hoagy Carmichael's 'My Resistance is Low' – and the rest of us would take it up as far as the next hill, when shortage of breath brought it to a choking conclusion.

Casual singing came more naturally in those days. Music lessons were part of the primary school curriculum and, at secondary level, hymns were sung at morning assembly, whilst churchgoing communities were raised in the choral tradition. People in pubs, before jukeboxes intruded, gathered to sing around the piano. Soldiers sang on the march, national servicemen in their billets. The folk tradition, as epitomised later by Bob Dylan, was strong amongst university students. Fifties' crooners articulated the words rather than just plain yelling, mumbling or unintelligibly gabbling which, post Beatles, has become the high decibel fashion amongst pop singers. No wonder the traditional songs are favoured by Karaoke practitioners.

Each year in October, the club held a championship in the form of a 'mountain' time trial from Sheffield to the Strines Inn, high up on the moors of the Yorkshire-Derbyshire border. With some trepidation, I put my name forward. The distance was well over twice what I'd raced before and the terrain unremittingly hilly, with a couple of one in five climbs towards the end. It was a severe test and I feared I might suffer the humiliation of having to walk across the finishing line, shoving my bike, utterly exhausted.

My clothing and equipment didn't augur well for a good performance. The Langsett track bike was light and lively enough, but my Sturmey Archer three speed hub-gear had a bottom ratio too low for most climbs and a top too low for most descents. In any case, the Sturmey's multi-cog gearing squandered energy.

It was a chilly start, but then out came the sun. I was horrendously overdressed – heavy woollen jersey, shirt, vest, linen shorts and a pair of leather motor cycling gloves that came half

194

way up my forearm. I carried no drinks bottle and in no time was sweating heavily and probably dehydrated. But I plugged on, and to my amazement, recorded the best junior time. I was club junior champion at the first attempt.

I sat on a bench in the bar of the Strines Inn feeling elated, but trying not to look smug. It wasn't good to be perceived as a big head. One of the senior members bought me a glass of lemonade and from the way the others were staring at me I had the impression they'd only just realised I was a member. I kept quiet, but I recall thinking: what if now I train really hard, what else can I achieve?

I went home and with a small pot of red paint wrote in plain view across the centre of my handlebars, 'Je peux. Je dois. Je veux.' [I can. I must. I will.] The triumph of the will might have fired Hitler's ambitions at the 1936 Olympics, but, ironically, it was also what drove some of Britain's greatest achievements, including victory over the Nazis. I was trying to psyche myself up to maximum effort, and some friends thought it a bit extreme. But within the year, following a string of strong performances, I was to become National Junior Road Racing Champion and then their criticism turned to adulation.

First Junior in the Sheffield R.C.C. Mountain time trial

195

The Sheffield Mercury team at the start of the 1951 Baslow Junior road race

BLRC National Junior Road Racing Champion

PUSEY AND ME – ALTER EGOS

The effect of cycling's embittered civil war in the 1940s and 50s was to split the sport into two quite distinct schools of racing perfectly exemplified by the early careers of Bernard Pusey and me. For aspiring roadmen before 1952 the choice was stark. Either you joined the 'rebel' BLRC and partook of their many Continental-style road races, some whose mountainous terrain palely ghosted the Alps and Pyrenees; or you joined the NCU for the straitjacket of track racing, plus the odd little titbit of massed-start on some relatively flat and dreary closed circuit around an army camp, aerodrome or motor racing venue – about as glamorous as donning wellies and waltzing with your granny. To me it seemed a 'no-brainer'. Racing in my native Peak District brought me close in spirit to the real action on the Continent as portrayed in *But et Club* and *Miroir Sprint*. For, make no mistake, being a League man was a quasi-spiritual experience. In reality you couldn't bestride your machine and become Coppi, Koblet or Bobet, but racing with the League at least enabled you to light a candle at your hero's shrine. You need not be a star yourself. However lowly your race position, however rapidly you went off the back on the first climb, you were still, nevertheless, ennobled just by taking part. You won your spurs by suffering to the best of your ability. Even better, you became a rebel in an age of deference, before adolescence was empowered by rock 'n' roll music and wooed by commerce. As a red-blooded BLRC rebel defying timid orthodoxy, you could, if you wished, regale your fizzing hormones in colourful, eye-catching garb, sport your emblematic musette and sunglasses (on the dullest of days) and sally forth yelling 'Up the League' – teenage exhibitionism about as 'cool' as it got in the monochrome Fifties.

Later I came to realise it wasn't that simple. I had overlooked two salient facts. One was, of the two rival organisations, only the long established NCU had UCI recognition and therefore the whip hand over international selection. It was all very well being a glamorous rebel and having the best of British racing, but if you had ideas to progress beyond your station and compete at World Championship, Olympic and Commonwealth Games level – indeed in any UCI event over the Channel – an NCU licence was essential (though, amusingly, the once and always staunch League man Doug Petty recently confided he had got by nicely in Belgium by forging his 'NCU licence').

Secondly, to be a top dog in the League was not necessarily to be a top dog in Britain. There existed an enormous pool of latent talent in the Union closed-circuit ranks – riders of the calibre of Haskell, Des and Brian Robinson, Vines, Gerrard, Maitland, Tiny Thomas, Krebs, Proctor, Blower, Brittain, King, Wilmott, Eric Thompson (British Empire and Commonwealth Games champion), the incomparable Ray Booty, who could turn his hand to anything on two and three wheels, and, of course, Bernard Pusey himself (some, of course, at times holding joint NCU/BLRC membership) – I could go on and on, because that pool of NCU talent was arguably wider than its BLRC counterpart, unsurprisingly so since it drew on a membership thirty times larger. There were, I realised, challenges to be had outside the limited scope of my League licence.

By 1952 those twin-track schools of racing began to come together. The trigger for that slow merger was the 1951 Tour of Britain. Backed by a major newspaper, it proved an enormous publicity coup for the BLRC and cast the fuddy-duddy NCU in a poor light. With cycle trade participation and the consequential expansion of professional racing, pro-team managers began headhunting talent from the NCU's top echelons. As it progressively lost its stars to the League, so its general membership declined. Clearly, the game was up. The Union was forced to adopt road racing. But it made little practical difference on the ground. There would be no single racing licence until the two bodies formally merged in 1959.

Bernard's path to the top via the orthodox NCU and mine via the rebel League began separately, but then converged as we first competed against each other at home, then finally abroad as allies in the same teams. It was common at top rider level for past allegiances to be disregarded and politicking left aside. The common experience of racing together as national servicemen also did much to blur this distinction. Your badge of origin was well known, but seemingly irrelevant in face of the prime necessity to rub along together and conduct the business in hand: getting fit, going fast and trying to outwit the opposition.

And yet, recently visiting Bernard at his home in Derby to research this piece, I was intrigued to discover this former 'Union-Bod' harboured something of the rebel lefty me of sixty years ago. In uneasy proximity on his dining room table lay copies of the satirical 'boat rocking' *Private Eye* and the 'steady as she goes' *Telegraph* ('We buy it for the crossword and a good laugh at Disgusted of Tunbridge Wells'). This cultural gulf reminded me of the ancient confrontation that had once divided us. The years had passed and here we were now sharing much the same taste. In conversation, we unearthed other commonalities: working class parents, for example, just making ends meet. How in front of our mums we'd tipped out our weekly wage packets to pay for our bed and board – in that pre-welfare era, scrounging was not the done thing and just about everyone worked and lived without state subsidy.

Then there was the Yorkshire connection. Not only did Bernard, like me, marry a Yorkshire lass, but also might never have become a cyclist if his mother hadn't herself been born and bred in God's Own County (cue for brass band and pudding with gravy). It was an 'Eeh bah gum' cousin cycling 200 miles down to the Pusey family home in Surrey that first stirred his interest in biking. The young cousin wasn't a 'proper cyclist', nor was pedalling such a great distance on a sports cycle all that unusual for the time – it was just what ordinary youngsters did in the *Boys' Own* spirit of adventure that then prevailed, when many parents saw adolescent risk-taking as 'healthy' and part and parcel of growing up. (As for me, aged 15 and with parental approval, I cycled off on solo youth hostel trips to Wales and Northumbria, incommunicado for ten days save for the odd postcard home to prove I was still alive.)

However, though Bernard was not immediately inspired to become a racing cyclist – his Continental career as a full-time professional with Hercules lay in the distant future – he saw the bike as a something for nothing way to get about and save on bus and train fares. He began aping his cousin with 70-mile round trips to Brighton and other South Coast resorts. 'I wasn't much good at ball games,' he confesses, 'but biking seemed to be something I took to naturally once I got the idea. I went for tear-ups with the local lads and usually came off best.'

Mechanics was something else he took to naturally. Youthfully impecunious, he assembled his first half decent bike from odds and ends, rescuing the frame itself off a scrap heap. Leaving Kingston Technical College at 16, he found unhappy employment as a trainee electrical engineer with a firm in Lambeth ('a bit oppressive') and about the same time from a newsagent picked up his first copy of *Cycling* magazine. There he read about the exploits of George Fleming (contemporary 50-mile time trial record holder and winner of the 1947 Paris–London) and promptly joined his hero's South London based Belle Vue CC, a mistake, he admits, as after work he had to stay behind an hour or more to participate in club activities, then cycle 15 miles home in the dark. It was an exhausting routine and he soon switched to the much closer Redhill CC (by this time he had graduated to a second-hand F H Grubb grass track machine with lay-down angles and a wheel base the length of a hockey pitch). His first race was a Novices 25-mile time trial at Staines under RTTC rules, the modest time of 1.12.15 giving no hint of his true latent ability. Referring to this event, Bernard says, 'I raced in a shirt with a collar and tie. My mum, going through her Christian phase, had enrolled me in the Boys Brigade (motto 'Sure and steadfast'). I was due on parade in Tadworth later that morning and had to tear straight off after the race with no time to change. In all I rode 65 miles before answering the bugler's call and marching through the streets in that very same sweaty, smelly shirt.'

Sure and steadfast might also describe Bernard's early racing career. His time trials were solid but not outstanding performances, likewise his first NCU 100-kilometre massed start race on the closed circuit at Goodwood – by his own estimate 'not brilliant'. Gradually, however, he learned how to position himself in the bunch and at sprint finishes, how to read a race and not waste energy on futile attacks and pursuits. From dabbling on the track, mainly at Herne Hill (he became 50-mile tandem-paced National Champion), he acquired a sharper turn of speed. Once he got the knack and muscled up and toned his physique, there was no stopping him and he enjoyed a succession of wins, his best at Blandford army camp and Church Lawton aerodrome against top opposition.

Since he appeared to have been a born roadman, I queried why he hadn't joined a League club. His answer is typical of someone whose only source of information came from the censored pages of *Cycling* magazine. 'It wasn't I had anything against the BLRC. It was just that I knew nothing about them.'

By 1951 he was NCU Southern Counties massed start champion. His outstanding ability was finally recognised by the international selectors when in 1952 his name was added to the short list for the Helsinki Olympic Games. A year later he finished close second in the NCU Road Racing Championship behind Ted Gerrard.

National service was a fact of life in the 50s for young men like us. Bernard had his service deferred to complete his Higher National Certificate in Electrical Engineering, but aged 21 he could put it off no longer. In the six months prior to call-up, he filled in with a job labouring on a building site, which he now describes as a course in weights. On his first day he carried twenty 100 cwt bags of plaster (i.e. a ton) up a 100-yard slope, mixed it all by hand and shovelled it into tubs, which he then had to lug up two flight of steps. The total weight with water added was five tons! 'No gloves supplied, my hands were just one big blister and I was close to collapse. Luckily, it was a Friday and I had the weekend to recover.' He stuck it out and those six months of hard labour were to perform wonders for his upper body strength and powers of endurance.

After all that, he says, square-bashing was a doddle. And eventually his two years in army uniform turned out to be no bad thing. In charge of the Army Cycling Union was the go-ahead Captain Bourne, who arranged for a team (Peter Proctor, Les Willmott, Brian Robinson and Bernard) to take part in the Route de France, the amateur version of the TDF, alongside an NCU England team (Brian Haskell, Dick Henley, Des Robinson and Alan Ashmore).

Imagine what that must have been like. It was at a time, 1952, when few ordinary Brits travelled abroad much less raced there. Here our lads, whose formative experiences had been mostly on flattish, closed circuits, found themselves competing against the foreign amateur *crème de la crème* on their home patch. 'We all felt we had something to prove,' says Bernard, 'and we set off attacking and madly chasing down every break. We wasted oodles of energy and paid for it when we reached the Pyrenees.' I asked him for his most vivid memory. 'Hurtling down a col at 50 mph and being suddenly confronted with a long, dark tunnel. You went blind. Outside it was brilliant sunshine – you wore sunglasses – inside, pitch black. You gripped the bars tight, aimed for that tiny ring of light that marked the exit and just hoped for the best. It was mayhem as riders panicked, braked and collided. You could see the sparks jumping as their pedals scraped the tarmac or tunnel walls.' We agreed that nowadays tunnels would be safely floodlit – but no such thing as 'duty of care' existed in those wild and woolly days of the cotton racing cap!

At the end of one such stage Dick Henly was missing. A search party was despatched only to find him lying off road part way down a precipice. He had ruptured his spleen. The hospital fees cost the

NCU a small fortune and henceforward they insisted that riders pay for their own personal insurance as a condition of selection.

Like Bernard, National service for me was no bad thing either – no international selection but time off to train and race. I nearly won the 1953 Isle of Man Viking Trophy Race in RAF colours but was caught coming off the mountain into the teeth of a howling gale and had to be content with fifth and King of the Mountains. In RAFCA races the strict rules concerning pro and amateur held no sway. Several times I crossed swords with the Hercules's professional, Frederick Otmar Krebs, but was always pipped in the sprint. Fred had his airs and graces and was notoriously unsociable towards anyone he deemed beneath him (most people it seems from my conversations with his contemporaries). My RAF Stafford team mate Norman Purdy once got up to him in a solo break, only to be put in his place with 'that's impossible – you must have taken a tow from a lorry'. Though a mere Leading Aircraftsman like the rest of us, LAC Fred unscrupulously traded on his ambiguous initials. Signing himself in as F. O. ('Flying Officer') Krebs, he could acquire concessions and privileges above his lowly rank, or so he claimed.

Though Bernard's national service stint and mine overlapped, very few of the races we took part in were genuinely inter-service and we cannot recall ever competing together. One inter-services event, however, did take place regularly at Saighton Army Camp, near Chester. Bernard won there in 1952 and I was a close second to Willmott the following year. I remember our Stafford team being lodged in a dilapidated Nissan hut with a big, draughty hole in the wall beside my bed. It looked as if a giant rat had sharpened its teeth. We joked it was where someone on the Escape Committee had made his last desperate bid for freedom. This army camp was grim and stalag-like – though, Bernard assures me, no worse than many others. By contrast, our RAF Stafford, in retrospect, resembled a five-star hotel.

Service life for those sportsmen with home postings to the right camp could be comparatively cushy. Both Bernard and I were granted time off to train and race – in season as much as three days a week. It was somewhat like being a part-time professional of the 'amateur' kind that was commonplace behind the Iron Curtain. Sometimes, unashamedly, we exploited this privilege to our own advantage. Once at RAF Stafford, being tardily informed of a race cancellation after our passes had been issued, we kept mum and took off anyway for a three day touring holiday, including one cheeky night at the host camp ('Cancelled, sergeant? Never! First we've heard about it'). Bernard remembers a trip to a stage race in Belgium at the behest of Captain Bourne. He and the team were under orders to return immediately afterwards to compete on the Isle of Man, but he ducked out. 'I'd enjoyed Belgium so much I thought, "Sod it, I'm staying put for a few more races".' (About the same time, Wearwell's talented Trevor Fenwick was a lone pioneer in Belgium, finishing eighth in the independent category version of Het Volk just behind rising star Fred Debruyne, and later winning at Moustier sur Sambre, beating many top Belgian riders in the process and becoming the first British semi-pro to achieve that distinction.)

Captain Bourne must have been a very understanding man. Giving the two-fingered salute to an officer was a hanging offence, yet Bernard got off scot-free.

Despite national service being a relatively cushy number for Bernard and me, we confided we were glad to be shut of it. He was demobbed in December '53 and I in October '54. We had no explanation for why that first year of freedom for both of us turned out to be one of our most successful. I went on to win the Dover–London, Scottish 3-Days and Tour of Britain, whilst Bernard achieved a number of victories, including the prestigious, seven-stage Tour of Ireland , plus third in the British Empire and Commonwealth Games road race at Vancouver.

The Eire Tour formed part of *An Tóstal*, the name for a series of festivals celebrating Irish life and culture. Inaugurated in 1953, it continued on into the early 1960s, when it eventually died out. Held in early spring with the object of drawing tourists during the Easter off-season, there was no guarantee of good weather. The 1954 version was notorious, not just for the snowstorm on stage 5 that prompted a mass abandonment and reduced the field from 108 starters to 15 finishers, but also for the death of 19 year-old English rider, Denis Weston (Long Eaton CC), in the most gruesome circumstances, impaled on the shaft of a cart.

Bernard gave notice of his intentions by winning the first stage, Dublin–Athlone. But it was the manner of his winning that caught the eye. In the breakaway with John Kennedy (Scotland) and John Lackey (Ireland), he took off alone and crossed the line with a lead of five minutes. And it was not that the rest were slouching – the average speed for the 145 miles was over 26 mph. 'I just felt I had the legs for it,' he says – surely something of an understatement. It was fortunate that stage two, skirting what later became 'bandit country', happened well before 'The Troubles', or British riders might have had to be issued with bulletproof vests. As it was, the last stage was ceremonial, or a 'club run' as *Bicycle* called it, with riders wrapped up in an odd assortment of clothing against the intense cold. Contemporary photographs show a service lorry piled high with abandoned bikes from the storm and Bernard being chairlifted by his triumphant team mates at the award ceremony.

Bernard dug out the *An Tostal* trophy for me from amongst his souvenirs. It is even weirder than the Paris-Roubaix cobblestone, being like an early battleshield of the fabled giant Finn McCool – round, solid bronze, inscribed with ancient Celtic hieroglyphics and fantastically heavy – handy for weight training, he joked.

The An Tóstal trophy

Unsurprisingly, he was now being headhunted to turn professional. An offer came from former Manchester track star, Syd Cozens, to join BSA, then led by Bob Maitland, but before this could happen Cozens, a notorious wheeler-dealer, had switched allegiance to Hercules, supplanting as manager the long established former time trial champion, Frank Southall, in the process. The original 1953 four-man Hercules team of Derek Buttle, Dave Bedwell, Clive Parker and Dennis Talbot had, by 1955, swelled to ten, including Tony Hoar, Maitland, Krebs, Brian Robinson and Bernard. They were based together on the Côte d'Azur at Les Issambres and were competing in all the big races. Cozens, 'a bandit' according to Robinson, had his hands on a rich purse of £100,000 (Dracula and blood bank come to mind), and the riders lived well – though maybe not so well as Cozens himself, spending money like water as Hercules, the company, slid down the road to perdition!

At the villa they had a Maid Madeleine to wash, cook and clean for them. According to Maitland, who disapproved of some of the team's antics, Krebs amused himself by teaching this naïve young French lady to curse like a trooper under the guise of tutoring her in standard English. Each morning, to general merriment, she would greet them at breakfast with a smile and a formidable volley of effing and blinding. Oh, what larks!

The Hercules villa at Les Issambres

They were expected to train and race on the Hercules standard production line 'Tour de France' model, which Bernard describes succinctly as 'crap'. It had not alloy but steel handlebars and also ordinary steel tubing, instead of the prestigious 531 common to most other lightweights. In disgust, Maitland reverted to his old BSA frame, after having it re-sprayed in Hercules's colours. Bernard blamed the crap bike for a dip in form and had A S Gillott build him a frame, which he paid for from his own pocket. He hand painted it in dark blue and affixed some gold 'Hercules' transfers. Cozens failed to notice the swap until the World Championships at Frascati. 'It was Bedwell, the bloomin' idiot,' Bernard said. 'He'd been a frame builder and he was pointing at the lugs, which were a bit fancy. 'That's not a Hercules,' he blurts, 'it's a Gillott.' Cozens overheard and I thought he might go bananas and kick me off the squad. But all he said was, 'They're not paying you, are they?'

In fact, Cozens eventually recognised the problem and without consulting with the riders had Mercier make him some mock Hercules frames. However, the angles were so laid back that the team rebelled and refused to ride them.

The worst equipment problem they faced was with their tubular tyres, which were supplied by Dunlop and, unlike the frames, couldn't be faked. (There were strong and long-standing commercial ties between Hercules and Dunlop going back 30 years.) The team was promised a £200 bonus each for riding these Dunlops, but it wasn't long before they noticed that they were suffering twice the number of punctures of any other team. Cutting one open, they discovered why. The date stamp inside was less than three months old and the immature rubber hadn't had time to harden. Robinson, always the most independently-minded member of the outfit, ignored Cozens and Dunlop and cycled over the border into Italy to buy his own tyres Chez Barale, as I was to do in 1957.

The accursed Dunlops caused Bernard's early exit from the 1955 Tour de France. Krebs punctured on stage 2 from Dieppe to Roubaix and Bernard waited behind to help him back up into the shelter of the convoy. There Bernard himself punctured, an event that went unnoticed in the British team car. He fitted the spare tyre he was carrying strapped beneath his saddle, but within five miles punctured again. This time, with no spare, he was forced to continue on the flat tyre, bumping over the cobblestones and scarcely able to keep his bike upright. He arrived at the stadium to find the gates shut and staff and officials gone home. He was counted out of time and so automatically eliminated.

One of his best rides for Hercules was in the Grand Prix Catox at Marseilles (Catox was a French stock cube akin to Oxo). What happened there is worthy of mention, if only because it illustrates a classic team tactic. With about 25 miles of the race left, the Frenchman Siguenza was out in front alone. His nickname was 'Zig-Zag', so perhaps the peloton had permitted his escape on health and safety grounds. Anyway, approaching the city on the final loop, Bernard decided to try to close the gap on his own. 'There were lots of cobbles and tramlines,' he says, 'so with all my Belgian experience I felt quite at home.' He sprinted away but took Zig-Zag's team-mate Bultel with him. 'Each time I turned round looking for help, there he was, grinning and yelling "Allez!" Of course, when I catch Siguenza, off goes Bultel, and now it's Zig-Zag's turn to sit on my wheel (again with safety in mind, best place for him you might think!). I thought, what choice do I have? If I give up now, the peloton will mow us down and I'll have wasted all that energy for nothing. Siguenza sits in behind until he's nicely recuperated and then he attacks me and I can't respond. It finishes with a La Perle one-two, but at least I hold off the peloton and get third place. I was probably the strongest rider there and could have won, but it's no good fretting. That's the game. I'd have done exactly the same in their place.' To their credit, after the race the two men from La Perle-Coupry came over to apologise and commiserate. And next year Bernard himself was sponsored by the same marque, so it was not all wasted effort.

The report in *Miroir Sprint* carried a photograph and the words *'Pusey effectue un travail d'Hercule pour rejoindre Siguenza'* (Pusey accomplishes a labour of Hercules to catch Siguenza). Contemporary French journalists loved to demonstrate their classical learning. They also revelled in 'witty' caricatures of the riders, especially of foreigners. Bernard's lean and sharply profiled phizog attracted comparison with a fox, and respected journalist Blondin remarked drolly that he could have done service as the quarry in an English county hunt.

Bernard was not always so sanguine when it came to the behaviour of Continental riders. I asked him about the 1955 Tour of Britain, when in the sprint finish at Phwelli he pulled the Italian Mattivi back by the saddle and was demoted from first to last place. 'It wasn't something I did habitually, but he really got my goat. He'd done no work in the break, sat at the back all the way pulling faces and trying to scrounge food and drink. Then come the last 200 yards and he's off like a bloomin' rocket.' Neither man bore a long-term grudge, however. When next they met up in Belgium, they shook hands and Mattivi was 'as good as gold' thereafter.

Around April 1955, the ten-man Hercules team, with masseur Schramm and its English mechanic, decamped from Les Issambres northwards to be close to Paris. (One imagines Madeleine on the doorstep, duster in hand, waving them off with tears in her eyes as she fondly mouths her tiny English vocabulary of Krebsian oaths). Cozens had very expensive tastes for a former bike rider and they settled into a posh *auberge* in the village of Poigny-la-Foret near Rambouillet. The cooking was *cordon-bleu*. Bernard remembers it as a chocolate box idyll of a place at the heart of an enchanting forest. Nothing, it seems, was too good for sybaritic Syd – he fiddled as Hercules's cash burned holes in his pocket. From time to time his middle-aged track racing associates would pop up for a bit of a jolly with their old pal whilst the team was out training – there seems little doubt who footed the bill. Even the hotel owner, Viel, a *soigneur* at Six-Day events, was part of Syd's social network. The name Bambagiotti keeps cropping up – he was an Italian from Cita Di Castello married to a French girl and pre-war had competed with Syd in Australia. Here he was engaged as 'the expert on Italian racing', though one wonders how this was justified as the team rarely raced in Italy.

And then there was the question of salaries. It had been assumed each rider was on the same footing with a generous salary of £1000 per annum, that is until the mechanic made an enforced trip back to Britain and there somehow got his eyes on the payroll. When he returned, he let the cat out of the bag. Maitland was being paid more than everyone else. Cozens, his old boss at BSA, had in secret arranged a special deal for him. When news of this broke at the hotel, there was hell to play and Cozens was accused of favouritism. Robinson, in particular, was outraged because his strong performances (eighth in Paris–Nice, fourth in the classic Flèche Wallonne and top of the leader board for much of the Tour of the Six Provinces) had done most to bring the name of Hercules to public attention. He and Cozens already shared a mutual dislike and now it was out in the open. Team morale inevitably suffered.

The atmosphere was already strained because Robbo felt some of his compatriots were not pulling their weight, nor had they adopted the right attitude of mind for success abroad. They needed to toughen up and, like him, become more single-minded, learn from the Continentals and race to win. Living this soft 'holiday-camp', apartheid-style life under Cozens had not helped to make them lean and hungry enough.

Bernard is also critical. He speaks of some of his team mates who never seemed to finish a race much less contest one, of a rider in particular who gobbled every scrap of food put before him and then some more only to vomit it all back as soon as he got on his bike, almost like a bulemic.

It was all to end in tears. The dream of a British professional team racing full time on the Continent was over. The Tour of Britain that autumn proved to be Hercules's last throw before, almost bankrupt, it was eventually taken over and finally merged with Raleigh in 1960. The team was disbanded. Some, like Krebs, disillusioned, gave up altogether. Others, like Robinson and Bernard, soldiered on abroad – Robinson with the gritty self-belief that was his trademark and was to inspire imitation from later generations, including Vic Sutton, Jock Andrews and myself*.

Bernard had no enthusiasm for returning to the part-time humdrum racing scene in Britain. The life of full-time pro on the Continent might be incredibly tough – especially so for a foreign interloper – but at least it was far more exciting, adventurous and challenging than the wage slavery he had experienced back home. He was unusual for a journeyman cyclist of that era in managing to eke a living for most of his career entirely from the sport – even Robinson spent the winters in England working as a builder in the family business. In the off-season Bernard never took time out, but instead raced on the indoor track in Copenhagen. There he linked up with Cyril Peacock and Ken Mitchell – the international aspect of the spectacle serving to boost attendances. They lodged rent free with an Anglophile family and took whatever contracts the stadium managers offered – omniums, 3-hour Madisons, bit parts in Six-Day races. It was cuthroat and utterly exhausting and Bernard knew, short of a miracle, he would never become rich from it. But he had the mind set of a dedicated professional and, unlike some of his Hercules compatriots, grabbed whatever chances came his way.

---

* Our adventures are recounted in my previous book, *In Pursuit of Stardom.*

He recalls the hot, stifling atmosphere of the ill-ventilated stadium. 'The stale air was blue with tobacco smoke and for hours on end you were pulling this muck into your lungs. One night after a hard session I started cycling back to the digs feeling drained of energy. Then, after a few minutes outside in the cold fresh air, it was like I'd had a blood transfusion. It must have been the oxygen coursing through my veins. I suddenly felt wonderful.'

In the spring of 1956, post-Hercules, he and Robinson clubbed together to rent a small villa close to Les Issambres. 'It was a waste of time. Unbelievably for the Côte d'Azur it snowed, even on the coast. First time for fifty years. It was piled up high at the front door and it was as much as we could do to go shopping in Brian's Vauxhall Velux. Racing was cancelled. Cycling was out of the question.'

It says much for the character of the two impecunious young men that they were not put off by such bad luck. Robinson returned to England to sell his car, using the cash to re-launch his bid for recognition. The rest is history.

The weather was much milder in 1958, and a good job too. 'I'd spent the winter racing in Copenhagen before heading south in my Citroën. In Ghent I picked up Ian Brown and Ron Coe. We rigged up a makeshift bed in the back and took it in turns to drive 1000 miles virtually nonstop to avoid hotel bills. When we arrived, Stan Brittain joined us from the Simplex training camp and together we rented this awful budget chalet. It was like bits of hardboard glued and nailed together. We called it "The Cardboard Box". There was just one big bed that pulled out from the wall and we all four slept in that – or tried to. The mattress was wafer thin and there was a wooden bar across the middle where the bed folded. It stuck into you all night long, whichever way you turned, and was absolutely crucifying.'

Perhaps crucifixion and sleep deprivation should have their place in the training manuals, because it was here in the Grand Prix International de Monte Carlo that Bernard scored one of his finest victories. Jock, Vic and I were staying close by in our ambulance and also took part. The course consisted of three laps of a circuit, each with an ascent of the Moyenne Corniche. I was making a comeback after a six-month complete lay off and found the going very hard. Nevertheless, I was still in contention in the peloton second time up the mountain when there was a sudden shower of rain. On the descent towards Nice, as we negotiated the bends, our fleeting shadows reflected off the glassy-wet tarmac and you could see riders repeatedly shifting their balance, trying to keep upright on the corners and yet remain as aerodynamic as possible, all without touching their brakes – sudden showers like this are always riskier than long downpours, which wash the road surfaces clean. At the bottom, the course swung left off the main road and up a very steep little hill through a small industrial estate to join the coast road back to Monte Carlo. It wasn't necessary to brake – you could just whoosh on up this narrow lane – but one idiot did brake, skidded and came off followed by others. The pile-up completely blocked the lane. Vic and I had to dismount and pick our way through. The hill was so steep it was hard to get going again from a standing start. We had to run and we never made it back to the front half of the bunch, though we caught tantalising glimpses of them going hell for leather in the distance.

So it was we abandoned at the end of the lap, got changed and joined the crowds gathered on the seafront to witness a rare, if not unique, British one-two, Bernard overcoming Coe in the sprint.

Grand Prix de Monte Carlo, 1958: a Frenchman
followed by Ron Coe (2nd in line) and Bernard Pusey (4th)

Pusey outsprints Coe to win the GP de Monte Carlo

Whilst Coe and Brittain returned to England, Bernard and Ian went to their base in Northern France, close to the Belgian border. Ian's roots, like mine, were with the BLRC (Lune RCC). He was the ideal companion for Bernard, 'a perpetual ray of sunshine, someone who could laugh his way through every setback, a joke a minute.' Bernard and I agreed that Ian's optimism was infectious and inspirational. Together they scraped a living from whatever races came their way, kermesse and classic alike. And it was here in May that our paths crossed again when, thanks to Ian's initiative, we combined to form British teams in the Tour de L'Oise, Tour de Champagne and later the Tour de L'Ouest, adventures all described in *In Pursuit of Stardom*.

Whilst our converted ambulance living quarters rested on a camp site in Rheims, they were lodging with a family called Parmentier, close to the town of Namur, a cramped single room but again rent free. Bernard tells an amusing anecdote that for its breathtaking, hillbilly cheek sounds like something from a cycling version of *The Dukes of Hazard*. He was in a two-man break with a local rider approaching the finish of a race, when a car packed full of people pulled out of a side road and drew up alongside. 'It was all the rider's relatives,' Bernard says. 'All crammed into this car. They were yelling their heads off, offering me 10,000 francs to chuck the sprint. They said the win would be a shot in the arm for their boy's career. I did some quick mental arithmetic and we agreed. But afterwards I had a hell of a time getting my money, and then it was only 7,000 francs.'

Unsurprisingly, this chancy, entrepreneurial life-style slowly began to lose its charm. Living out of a suitcase, hand-to-mouth, was fine and dandy as long as you were young, but there came a time when you hankered for something more permanent and predictable. By 1959, aged 28, most of Bernard's racing was being done in Britain. In the early days of the newly formed BCF, he managed to have his professional status rescinded, which opened the way for him to race as an independent with Kent based Witcomb Cycles. He shone in the Milk Race Tour of Britain with a win at Whitley Bay, four thirds, a third place in the points competition and sixth on general classification. 'I had another stage in the bag,' he comments, 'but was misdirected close to the finish.'

Tour of Britain 1959: Pusey wins at Whitley Bay

213

We discussed drug taking. 'It was so common amongst riders, it was like energy drinks are today and the usage was blatant.' A team mate in Paris–Tours had observed the Belgian rider Germain Derijcke falling back to the team car for an injection. 'They would refer to it as a 'vitamin supplement', but who in his right mind would take vitamins in the middle of a race? It's a joke!' Derijcke was a prolific performer in the one-day classics, winning, amongst others Paris–Roubaix, the Tour of Flanders and Milan–San Remo. But like so many stars of that generation he died young, aged just 47, from a brain haemorrhage. 'They had no idea how they were damaging their health and even if they did they probably thought the glory was worth the gamble.' Bernard himself never gambled on drugs, but remains equivocal about other British riders. 'It was like a virus that passed from one rider to the next. As long as you were on your own you could stay outside the system.' It was when riders were recruited into top trade teams and lived alongside the Continentals that they were most exposed to temptation and, more importantly, the know-how of doping, what to use and when. 'You can imagine how hard it would be to ignore what was going on around you and not become part of the culture, especially if you thought your career depended on it.'

Bernard slipped out of racing in 1960. It was not a conscious decision on his part, but force of circumstances that caused him to hang up his wheels. He and Pat had just married and that was a turning point in life when he had to consider someone other than himself. But the clincher was catching chicken pox at the age of 30. This is normally a disease of childhood – caught in adulthood, it can prove serious with lasting ill effects. Even when the telltale rash disappeared, he was left for months feeling debilitated and without the energy to ride his bike. He had lived the dream for many years and now it was time to take stock and look elsewhere.

I have described Bernard and me as alter egos. Though our pathways into the sport were different, our Continental racing careers took a similar line. We both married and left the sport in the same year. We both went into the teaching profession at about the same time – and we both experienced some initial discrimination based on ignorance and intellectual snobbery. Bernard sought a place at a teacher training institute and had good reason to be confident of success – his Higher National Certificate counted as an above A level qualification. But some in the selection panel demurred when it came to his cycling background, querying why he had chosen to spend the previous six years 'out of the labour market', implying it had all been a waste of time. Bernard hit back, pointing out how his cycling career exemplified many of those very same qualities required to become a good teacher: self-reliance, the entrepreneurial spirit, organisational skills and a dogged determination not to give up when the going became tough. He overcame the sceptics and was accepted, and after a few years of teaching at Bradford Technical College went on to read for a degree in Electrical Engineering at Leeds University.

I asked him if he had any regrets. I was expecting him to mention some missed opportunity or twist of fate: maybe, for example, his unlucky dismissal from the 1955 Tour de France, his only stab at the world's greatest cycle race. His answer took me totally by surprise. 'I regret the four years I used six and three-quarter inch cranks. It started with the Hercules bike when I accepted what I was given. From that point, my form seemed to take a dip, but I never thought to question why until I returned to the shorter cranks in 1959 and found myself flying again.' So after fifty years what still bugged him was the length of a revolving metal lever, that quarter inch of solid alloy looming large in his memory. I had to admit I had never measured my own cranks. It would never have occurred to me that their size mattered. So in the end, after all our similarities, here was something to stand between us – the numeracy and practicality of an engineer's mind.

I was at the door, shaking hands and about to leave, when we two septuagenarians touched on the topic of gardening and our plans to plant early potatoes. How the great eighteenth century tongue-in-cheek philosopher Voltaire would have approved. I was reminded of his bullshit-busting character Candide, who returned from his adventure-strewn travels 'to cultivate his garden'. The metaphor seemed appropriate for the retiring racing cyclist who renounces the limelight for the ultimate fulfilment of getting back down to earth at home, as one day even the greatest of champions must also do.

THE DAY A BRITISH TOUR WAS LOST AND WON

It is often surprising how the final result in a stage race can be seen in retrospect to have turned on a single incident on a particular day. Chance often contributes to achievement. So it was that an unimaginable stroke of luck helped me to victory in the 1955 Tour of Britain.

The *Daily Express* Tours of Britain 1951-54 had snatched cycling from out of near obscurity and elevated it to the front page alongside news of politics, war and the Royal Family. Through their enthusiastic reportage, journalists like Sidney Saltmarsh stressed the topsy-turvy, incident packed nature of the cycle race and this encouraged big crowds to turn out and witness in person the sweat-shiny 'heroes' materialising off the page. Some for a brief time became household names: Steel, Russell, Tiny Thomas, Bedwell, Les Scales, Brian Robinson and so on. For those four glorious years when the race was such a huge sporting and commercial success story, there was serious talk of it in time rivalling the Tour de France – from little acorns do great oaks grow. The British League of Racing Cyclists' top officials, whose brainchild this had been, were cock-a-hoop. It seemed they had hit the jackpot. Road racing, which they had long championed in face of the cycling establishment's cynical opposition, had at last caught the public imagination in a way that matched only their wildest dreams, and the long-term ascendancy of 'Britain's own Tour' appeared self-evident.

But there was a fly in the champagne. Skulduggery was afoot. With its own membership falling in face of its rival's enhanced popularity, the National Cyclists Union could not afford to stand idly by and do nothing. Certainly it wanted cycling to succeed, to become headline news – but on its own terms, not at its expense. So after years of opposition and denunciation, it now suddenly saw the light and flip-flopped. Adopting road racing in 1952, as if just discovering its own birthright after 50 years of denial, it began a campaign either to wreck the Tour of Britain or take it over and run it under its own auspices. The policy was to ignore it in public but behind the scenes badger the proprietor of the *Daily Express* with letters of protest to the effect that the BLRC was a 'rebel' body without UCI legitimacy. The Communist bogeyman was probably also invoked as BLRC teams had participated in French races run by the rebel, union-inspired FSGT*.

Lord Beaverbrook must have been badly shaken to discover that cycling harboured such hatred within its ranks, a political divide to rival anything in the Houses of Parliament. He was caught in a cleft stick. To 'legitimise' the race was to entrust its organisation to the untried NCU, who clearly lacked the experience and personnel to step into the League's shoes. An organisational shambles would be very bad publicity for the newspaper. On the other hand, his staunch right wing convictions warned him off 'the rebels', though they had proved four times over they could do the job. No doubt he delayed in the hope the two rivals would reach agreement. But by 1955 he must have realised this was as far off as ever, a matter that deeply concerned the Ministry of Transport. Perhaps the race was too much of a political hot potato. In truth we can only guess the reason why Beaverbrook withdrew his support so suddenly and at such short notice from such a popular annual event, although John Dennis has told me:

> I served as Press Officer and was a friend of Albert Asher, the *Daily Express* Publicity Officer. The race was lost when Asher tired of the battle between the two organisations and the involvement of the UCI, and he put his energy into the new Formula One car racing. What a disaster!

For the BLRC, left abruptly in the lurch without a sponsor to pay the bills, it seemed like the end of the road. But the League had an old friend in Billy Butlin, who put his chain of holiday camps at their disposal and paid for a handsome trophy. With the cycle trade also chipping in, Doug Peakall took on the unenviable task of organising the race in six short weeks. That he succeeded was nothing short of a minor miracle.

The 1955 Tour was to be an eight-days, nine-stages affair, beginning and ending in London. Most of the big trade teams were signed up, Hercules being fresh from a season's pro racing on the Continent,

---

* Fédération Sportive et Gymnique de Travail - an internationalist, Communist sporting organisation, founded in the 1930s, suppressed by the Vichy government during the war and still going strong.

culminating in the Tour de France. There were also International and Belgian teams. One innovation was to be the participation of two teams of young, would-be professionals from London and Sheffield known as Aspirants; but these were very much seen as makeweight underdogs. It was a foregone conclusion that the experienced, better prepared and resourced professional teams would mop up.

The Aspirant class touched a raw nerve in the RTTC. Aspirants were defined as amateurs licensed to race with professionals and independents for one year, after which they must choose to revert to their former status or step up to the paid ranks. They were barred from receiving a wage or retainer, but could accept the fruits of sponsorship.

Though the Aspirant class was recognised by the UCI and the BLRC had broken no rules, it was too much for the ultra orthodox RTTC to bear. They unilaterally declared Aspirants to be professionals by another name and promised to ban them. None of this bothered Dick Bartrop, Mick Waterfield, Ted Wren, John Short and me. We had already written off the RTTC as fanatics locked into the past and unable to move on (think of a cycling equivalent of the Taliban). Relishing the prospect of getting some top flight experience mixing it with the pros, we all eagerly signed up for the Sheffield aspirant team with Sid Ellis as our manager and John Heath and Derek Lee as driver/mechanics. A public appeal was set up to help to fund the enterprise and we received assistance in the form of spares from Langsett Cycles. Simpkins of Sheffield supplied us with a carton of their energy-packed glucose tablets and loaned us one of their tall delivery vans to serve as our following vehicle. It was all cobbled together at the last moment, but we had one great advantage over the other aspirant team: we were all from the same Falcon Road Club and team spirit already existed. On the lurching, six hour drive to London down the old A1 we squatted uncomfortably in the back of the van along with our equipment, arriving at dusk outside the Russell Hotel, Bloomsbury, where I spent an almost sleepless night in an airless box-room, kept awake by all-night traffic roaring round the Square.

Organiser Peakall lived in Islington, gentrified in recent property booms but then a run-down, left wing London borough (In the 70s there was an anarchist bookshop there whose stock consisted entirely of stolen books!). He must have had influence with the local council, because the Tour started on Upper Street (the old A1) outside the town hall, sharing space with an ongoing market, costermonger barrows and all. A large crowd of spectators had assembled and the highway was completely blocked as the lord mayor delivered a speech of welcome before flagging us off in neutralised procession – only as far as Bignalls Corner, where we stopped for lunch before the start proper. Again there was a large crowd entertained by wall-to-wall sunshine and the quipping, gift of the gab Jimmy 'Oscar' Savile holding forth on the speaker.

The start of Day One - Bignalls Corner

I had already tasted professional racing two years previously. Aged 19, having just acquired my first-category racing licence, I took part in the South Staffs Grand Prix and the Charles Fox Memorial Race, where I finished a creditable 13th. Both races – one flat, the other extremely hilly – were conducted at what seemed to me a furious pace, convincing me the pros truly were an elite and to be competitive I would need to grow up and develop physically. With my curiosity temporarily satisfied, I put further participation at that level on hold.

But now I was 21 and much stronger, with two Amateur Circuits of Britain (amateur stage races to this day never surpassed for length and toughness) and a whole lot of other maturing experiences behind me. So I was not overawed, nor much surprised, when we set off at a heart-jerking lick to end up at Clacton with an average speed of 26 mph. Joe Christison (Viking), fourth overall in 1954, won the sprint and donned the yellow jersey.

Next day took us to another Butlin's camp at Skegness, a long haul of 152 miles across the Fens. It was here that the aspirants first served notice they were not along just for the ride. Dick had got himself into the break and he easily outsprinted former NCU champion Graham Vines (contemporary pro-independent champion) to win the stage and seize hold of race leadership.

Dick Bartrop wins at Skegness

Now the weather took a turn for the worse. The following day was a split stage, a 73-mile road race in the morning followed after lunch by a 37-mile time trial. Cold horizontal rain swept over the Fens and Lincolnshire Wolds driven on a strong gusty crosswind. Viking launched attack upon attack to regain the yellow jersey for Christison and finally the peloton broke up into groups, with Ken Mitchell (Wearwell), Ian Steel (Viking), the irrepressible Andrews, Fourneau (Belgium) and Mattivi (International) in the lead. Andrews won the sprint at New Holland from Mitchell and Fourneau, the latter wasting his chances by mistaking the 200 yards flag for the finish. Dick and I were in the second group having had to work hard to keep the deficit down to three minutes.

The only way then to cross the Humber from New Holland to Hull, where we lunched at the Pier Café, was by ferry. As the starting order for the time trial was the inverse of GC, some of the morning's stragglers, arriving late at New Holland, experienced a disconcerting double whammy. Missing the boat, some also missed their lunch. The Sheffield aspirant Ted Wren, low down on GC as a result of puncturing on stage one, was a case in point. As he disembarked from the ferry he was grabbed by an official and dragged, protesting, straight to the start line. Despite being famished, he was counted down and despatched like an empty parcel. Ted tells of how, after a few miles, he passed Bob Thom, the Viking team manager, sitting outside on a pub bench quaffing a pint of beer. Ted gesticulated hand to mouth, crying 'Food! Food!' as he rode by. To his credit, Bob bought Ted a sandwich at the bar and chased him down in the team van in a scene of inadvertent comedy reminiscent of some early Tour de France.

I had worked hard during the morning session to defend Dick's yellow jersey and decided it would be wise to save my energy in the afternoon by taking it relatively easy in the time trial. I saw myself henceforth in the role of *domestique* and never dreamed I would soon be challenging for the major honours. Accordingly I set off at a rather leisurely pace, sitting up, hands in the centre-bars position and chain in the small ring, with the object of just ticking off the miles. By now the rain clouds had dispersed and it had become warm with fitful September sunshine. I remained cruising, offering a big target to the breeze, until about halfway, when nearing Bridlington Ken Mitchell caught me for two minutes. He swished past in his super aerodynamic pursuit mode, adding me to the string of scalps he no doubt hoped to collect en route as an experienced master of the lone effort. I watched him steadily drawing away. Then his Wearwell team van smoothed on by and someone inside gave me a pitying glance. Perhaps it was that glance that got my goat. I switched to the drops and began winding up the pedals until the gap stopped increasing. Next I decided to put my 'big'un' in, 52x14. At once the gap began to diminish.

Before I was caught

And after

As I overtook Ken he gave me a glare and I fully expected him to respond with a further burst of speed. If so, I was cooked as I was now going all out. I stormed on, still in something of a rage, and didn't look back until I was stomping up the climb to Flamborough. To my surprise the road behind was empty. I had dropped the professional pursuiter who had ridden so well in the Tours of France and Spain. This psychological boost really set my adrenalin going. From this point on I threw caution entirely to the winds, hardly bothering to change out of top gear, tearing into the climbs and descents like a madman. At the finish I waited on the line to time Ken home. To my delight, my watch recorded he had lost nearly four minutes, the two he had earlier taken, plus a bonus for me of two more.

That evening in our Filey Butlin's chalet the Sheffield aspirants celebrated retaining the race lead. Viking's Joe Christison had won the time trial by a margin of 38 seconds from Dick, but it wasn't nearly enough. Dick remained in yellow. The next stage to Sheffield, won by Hercules's Tour de France *lanterne rouge* Tony Hoar, saw Dick, Mick Waterfield and me up there in the winning break and some of our less consistent rivals losing more ground.

Passing through Pontefract en route to Sheffield

Sheffield–Pwllheli, 168 miles, was a massive stage that took the race through the High Peak and Welsh mountains. Our aim was to keep the status quo, let 'safe' breakaways go and try to conserve our strength for the final sixty miles of exceptionally challenging terrain that lay before us. With 70 miles remaining, in the Vale of Llangollen, Doug Booker (Viking), with Continentals Mattivi and Albert, had established a lead, but as none was a threat we were unconcerned, and while Dick 'rested' in the peloton, I tried to cover every new attempt at pursuit. Chasing down one of these attacks, I found myself in a group with enough team representation to work together. We soon caught the Booker group and, as the time interval grew, I realised I had become race leader on the road. Nevertheless, for Dick's sake, I sat in and only attacked to win the time bonus at the summit of Blaenau-Ffestiniog. The stage win went to the Italian Mattivi.

Now I topped the GC with Ken Mitchell at around two minutes and Dick a further two minutes back in third place. With three stages left our roles inside the Sheffield team were reversed and Dick became my *domestique*. But the situation was volatile and we were agreed that if the chance arose for him to vault back into the top spot he should take it. Mitchell had another game plan. On the bumpy road to Cheltenham he took a prime and the resulting time bonus saw him claw back 30 seconds. Fortunately for us, the Belgian Guldemont engineered a lone break of 80 miles that at one time stretched to 10 minutes as the bunch played cat and mouse. Thirty seconds was all Guldemont had left at the finish in Cheltenham, but importantly for us he had mopped up the other time bonuses en route.

Two stages left and my advantage had been cropped to 1.13. I felt very vulnerable, especially when Mitchell tried to psych me out with the threat, 'I'm going to take your jersey off your back 30 seconds at a time.' His track experience gave him the edge in any sprint where a time bonus was up for grabs, and there were enough primes left for the threat to be real.

But whether through fatigue or poor tactics, he missed two big chances next day on the road to Bournemouth when the prime at Blunsdon fell to King of the Mountains Fourneau, and at Marlborough Hill to Hoar. So it all came down to the last stage, Bournemouth–London, 118 miles. With such a slender lead, the odds were still slightly against me and I was heavily reliant on the team to get me out of any trouble. It was to be no triumphant victory procession. Mitchell attacked remorselessly, but each time he turned round after one of his brutal, head-down assaults, I was there on his wheel. Then, to my great relief, a five-man break was established comprising Haskell, Talbot, Booker, plus the London aspirant Blissett and our man Ted Wren. That took care of the time bonuses, but still Mitchell refused to give in. He should have kept a better look out, however, for failure to do so probably cost him the race.

With about 40 miles remaining, I felt my front tyre bumping on the rim and did a swift wheel change with team mate Mick Waterfield. I tore back up to the bunch through the caravan. Mitchell, resting between attacks, hadn't even noticed that I was absent and so failed to take his best chance of victory. And so I retained my margin and went on to win the 1955 Tour of Britain.

Receiving the yellow jersey on the penultimate stage

The professionals had suffered a heavy and unexpected humiliation and afterwards must have undergone some soul-searching. How had they, in particular Hercules, allowed this to happen? All that topflight experience on the Continent – the Tour de France, Tour of Spain, Tour of Europe – and yet the very race their sponsors most wanted them to win, the home Tour, was ceded to a bunch of jumped up amateurs. It was a bitter pill to swallow.

There were three factors at play, in my opinion. Firstly, they seriously underestimated our ability and team spirit. All through they expected us to crack, not realising how well the fiendishly difficult and long Amateur Circuit of Britain had prepared us to endure the vagaries of a stage race. Secondly, like non-league part-timers against the Manchester Uniteds of the Premier League, the psychological onus to win is on the full-time professionals and the part-timers have nothing to lose. Add to this particular psychological disadvantage another: the Hercules riders knew by now that their contracts were not to be renewed. The Hercules directors had been shocked at the extravagant cost of sponsoring a professional team on the Continent and had decided to cut their losses and pull out. The racing team had performed well, but this had hardly registered with their sports-cycle customer base back in Britain and sales were falling. Most of these pros would now have to forego the glamour, passion and razzmatazz of the Continental bike race and either retire from the sport, as did the talented Fred Krebs, or return to its prosaic, poorly rewarded British version, crippled by conflict between the controlling bodies. It must have been a prospect that filled them all with gloom. What was expected to be the strongest team, Hercules, could do no better than finish third, with Bernard Pusey top rider in 12th place.

from L to R: Bill Thompson; Derek Lee; John Heath; Ted Wren; Mayor of Sheffield; Sid Ellis; Tony Hewson; Dick Bertrop; Mick Wolerfield; John Short

None of this detracts from our victory. I say *our* victory because it was a team effort in which everyone, including the support staff, played a part. It took determination, planning, guts and – yes– luck. Dick could easily have ended up overall winner instead of third. On the crucial stage to Pwllheli, when the roulette wheel stopped spinning, chance dropped the ball on my number and (to confuse the metaphor) I took it up with both hands and ran.

Pwllheli was crucial. But I maintain the moment I actually won the Tour occurred two days previously when I lost my rag with Ken Mitchell. It was that lucky glance from his team car that fired me up. The two minutes I took out of him in the time trial was a little more than I eventually needed. My winning margin at the finish line on Hampstead Heath was 1.13.

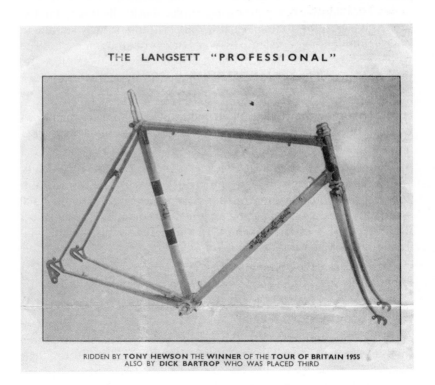

THE LANGSETT "PROFESSIONAL"

RIDDEN BY **TONY HEWSON** THE **WINNER** OF THE **TOUR OF BRITAIN 1955**
ALSO BY **DICK BARTROP** WHO WAS PLACED THIRD

THE OLD MAN AND THE BICYCLE

He knows how they vilify him, those conspiring hags. Emerging from the front door of his daughter's suburban villa, carrying his new bicycle over his shoulder, Reg glances to see them, two gardens down, in conversation together over the fence – malicious, middle-aged busybodies with shocking perms and eyes like hawks. Even with his back turned, he's aware they're watching him prop his machine up at an angle against a flower tub packed with scarlet and blue petunias, before gingerly bending to thumb the tyres. In half a sec one of these 'ladies' will wink at her companion. 'It's a good match, Mr. Preterite, your jersey and those flowers,' she'll call, indulging the bony arch of his backside with a patronising smile. 'Fuck!' he'll say, far too loudly to be just for his own benefit, whilst simultaneously smiling to himself and pressing a fist into his sore back as he straightens up. 'The fuckers are soft.' And now, without acknowledging their presence, he'll cleats-click-clack back inside the house for his track pump.

Witches!

'I don't know how she puts up with him,' Maureen breathes as he disappears, the bicycle already pressuring the tub into a slow sideward slide.

'No need to whisper, dear,' Patricia says. 'You could address him with a loud hailer, it's all water off a duck's back. I confronted him Tuesday last about cycling on the pavement. Might as well have spared my breath. Of course, he pretends he's deaf, but it's all an act to make people feel sorry for him. That daughter of his, she must be a saint.'

'Angela? That's nothing. What about his wife? Look what happened to her – he as good as killed her, poor soul.'

The tub abandons its struggle with gravity and topples over. The bicycle grounds with a clatter.

Maureen permits herself a thin-lipped smile. 'There it goes, three thousand pounds worth.' She mouths the numerals with evident distaste.

'For a push-bike? Three thousand? Is it gold-plated or something?' Patricia is incredulous. 'It's obscene. You could buy a car for less.'

'Boys' toys! It does sound mad. But then he is mad. Angela says she's at her wit's end with him. I could smell it on her breath when she spoke. Three thousand from his personal savings account – what's going to be left of her inheritance if he carries on like that?' They pout their disapproval of the mad, old spendthrift.

'What was it you were saying about murder?'

'Not exactly murder. There's more ways than one to kill. He did away with her by neglect.'

'His own wife?'

'Well, judge for yourself. Angela says he goes cycling with his selfish so-and-so buddy-buddies. They're always off out together in a pack – retired gentlemen like him, of course. And you know what that means. Too much time on their hands – the need to do something sweaty, get themselves thirsty, have a damned good excuse to indulge.'

Patricia gestures with a cupped hand.

'They all do it, these cyclists of a certain age, over exercising and drinking – goes straight to their brains, what little they have.'

Maureen nods. 'One day he comes home later than usual and more than a little under the weather – and she's not in the kitchen. So where is she, he wonders? And his dinner's not even waiting for him in the oven. He goes stamping upstairs in a strop and finds her in bed, curled up. He gives her a good hard shake. Maggie, he says, my dinner? Where's my dinner? No reply. Then suddenly it dawns. She's gone. Heart attack. Dead. If he'd been home where he should have been instead of gallivanting off with those other silly old fools, he could've called an ambulance and she'd be alive today.'

'Do you think he misses her?'

'Hard to tell now he's moved in here to sponge off his daughter, getting her running around at his every beck and call. According to Angela, he muttered to himself all through the funeral service, even when the vicar was ringing Margaret's praises, calling them a devoted couple and so on. It was awful, every other word an F something. She gave him a good elbowing, but it made no difference.'

At that moment, the old homicidal, self-indulgent, foul-mouthed reprobate re-emerges carrying a track pump and cussing eloquently on seeing his bike collapsed. Secretly smiling, he hoofs the tub aside and inflates the tyres.

229

Patricia gives Maureen a sly dig. 'Do you need any help with saving the planet, Mr Preterite?' No reply. 'He's having another deaf day.' They cackle.

'What *does* he look like,' says Maureen, 'dressing up in that gaudy cycling suit at his age.'

'It's all that Lycra, showing off their bony old bums. It makes them think they look young.'

The old man lobs the pump into the hallway, not bothering to shut the door. He mounts his machine with a grunt or fart, and he's off down the path, making a wobbly turn onto the pavement. He clicks his cleats into the pedals and accelerates past the two broomsticks to where a driveway connects with the road.

'What's Quick Step when it's at home?' Maureen squints at the dedication on his team-clothing top.

'It's a night club cum brothel in Barcelona, or so he's told Angela.'

* * * *

The breeze caresses the grey down of his bald, helmet-less head, all that's left of a once full forest of chestnut hair. Now his breath, propelled by effort, feels incandescent as though his dragon nostrils might be about to spurt fire. Now the slick tyres of his new carbon frame super-lightweight buzz down the asphalt highway, sounding the keynote of freedom. Escaping the pedestrian indignities of decrepitude – shuffling feet, quivering hands, muffled hearing, slow-witted explanations – he's young again, the bike lending him some mercurial sixth sense. King of the road, he negotiates the High Street traffic jam with an acquired sureness of touch. Weaving, swooping, he quickly takes himself to the head of the queue at the red light, and ignoring the horn blast from some envious motorist, occupies the inside lane. There, with one supporting hand on the steel barrier, he prepares to launch himself forth on the y of the yellow to be first at the next lights two hundred yards up ahead.

If only those blathering old bitches could see him now in his true element, they might show more respect. But they haven't a clue. How could they know he was a patriot who'd given two years of his youth to serve his country in the Korean War – a proper war, too, not like this overblown terrorist affair conjured up out of sweet F.A. Those

Chinks, they were proper warriors. Fifty-seven years or more and the memory of them still fresh – charging his Bren gun emplacement, wave on wave, hundred upon hundred, blowing their bugles and screaming death and destruction. But alongside his mates he stood firm. Oh yes, it had taken guts. 'Suicide bombers my arse, we faced down a whole bloody, slit-eyed, suicide division. Heroes we were. And are we old soldiers given credit? No, fat thanks we get. We're the forgotten army.'

From a wobbly push-off, he's third in the sprint to the next lights. He worms up to the front of the queue and rests a foot on the kerb. He's on the inside of a brand new maroon coloured Mini Cooper with white designer racing stripes and rap music blaring obscenities through the wound down windows. Bloody ignorant kids! He gestures to the youths inside to turn it down.

'No, you turn your fuckin' hearin' aid down, grandad,' the driver yells in response, showing tan tobacco teeth. His crew-cut mate in a Fcuk T shirt leans out of the rear window and sprays him from a sports drink bottle. 'Phwooar! You stink. You need to take a shower, you filthy old bastard!'

The sticky fluid mingles with sweat and runs down into his eyes, stinging him blind. Stranded as the light changes and the line of cars races past, he dabs his brow with his sleeve and plots revenge.

At the final set of lights, he halts a length behind the Mini. The grinning youth with the bottle is two fingering him through the window. He waits until the lights turn to red on the intersecting side street, counts to ten then push-foots himself up beside the car's rear wheel-arch. He takes another blast from the bottle and the youth's spittle full in the face, but this time he's ready. He has a coin in his hand, his lucky 1952 war penny. As the Mini revs up and pulls away, he leans across and lets it score a long, deep gash through the paintwork, exposing the bare metal beneath. The screech is music to his ears, like a chink taking a bullet to the belly. According to plan, he turns left into the one-way street against the traffic flow where the Mini can't follow and jumps up onto the pavement.

A squeal of brakes, the yob driver hits the pedal. Cars trapped behind begin hooting. Reg winds through the throng of pedestrians, shouting warnings for them to give way. Some respond angrily with 'What the hell does he think he's doing cycling on the pavement?' But this is an emergency and he doesn't give a shit, especially when he hears the slap slap of trainers and, glancing over his shoulder, observes the youths sprinting after him, shoulders pumping. A woman shopper screams as they shove past.

He even fancies he can hear their deep elastic gasping – then he's turning left at the T-junction, leaping the bike off the pavement and joining the slow, lane-swapping quarrel of traffic. Just scraping between a bus and lorry, he attains the outside lane. Surely they won't leave the pavement to cross two lines of traffic on foot? Surely they're not that mad? Now he's taking crazy chances himself, weaving in and out and around the vehicles any which side to overtake, then going right at the next lights just after they've turned red – cars coming at him flashing their lights and hooting – leaning the bike over at speed like a pro on a hairpin. Another half mile and he takes another right into a quiet side road that will lead him by a back route into the countryside, throwing his pursuers off the scent. Here he stops on a corner to look back. Nothing. They're nowhere to be seen. Just as he thought, the spotty louts haven't the heart or lungs even to run a mile. Fat chance they'd have charging with a bayonet. They're buggered already. Pathetic!

It's only then he realises his own scattershot heart is thudding like a mistimed trip-hammer and gulping at tides of arterial blood, throat scoured raw from the unaccustomed effort. When was the last time he felt this bad? Some long-ago head-down sprint finish to a 25, almost dying as he passed the kerbside timekeeper? Sweat trickles down inside his clothing. He feels clammy and hot and a little light-headed. But it's all been worth it. He's taught them a hard lesson, not to mess with a tough old guy like himself. And that paintwork is going to cost. They'll think twice next time.

A 4-wheel drive stops beside him and a young female passenger leans through the window. 'I say, are you OK? Only you look – we wondered –'

Ageism!

'Nothing wrong with *me*,' he snaps, adding under his breath, 'so buzz off.'

The girl smiles foolishly and the vehicle pulls away.

'Fuck,' he mutters. She must have observed him shaking. He pedals off on a roundabout route to the café rendezvous.

It's funny, Maggie dead two years and he never dreaming about her. Not once. Forty years married, living under the same roof, occupying the same bed and you'd think – well, it can't be right, falling into a dreamless sleep every night the moment his head touches the pillow. But now, pottering along in low gear, regaining his composure, she enters his mind. Perhaps it's the relaxing rise and fall of the pedals and hypnotic parade of landscape like a soothing green balm overlaying that first rush of triumph. Whatever, Maggie is here to fill the vacancy. Her dear face – at once he recognises that familiar expression of tender hopelessness, the chiding constant of their marriage. 'Where's your commonsense, Reg, getting yourself all hot and bothered from a silly scrape when there was no need? Why do you have to act so daft? You're seventy-seven, not a little kid.' The tone is of quiet despair.

'It's how I am, how I've always been. Too late now for me to change – but I do miss you, Mags.'

* * * *

The transport café, cinder car park lined with juggernauts and trailers, is the Wobblers' rendezvous, a big, glorified breezeblock shed with rusted metal windows steamed up from all-day breakfast cooking. The no-nonsense lorry drivers' menu – anything from an Eccles cake to curry with chips, instant coffee from a regiment size tin or tea the colour of molasses – offers Reg and his pals the sort of quick and easy comfort grub they grew up with. But today they're nowhere to be seen. A glance round the tables is all he needs to confirm they've already gone and given him up for dead. But just to be sure, he checks with a couple of drivers sitting near the door, beer gut bellies parked on the tabletop. Looking up from platefuls of sausage and egg swimming in HP sauce, they afford him a quizzical once-over from his bald bullet head to shoes that resemble dancing pumps.

'We did run across a bunch o' cyclists back at the roundabout,' chuckles one of the supersizers. 'Had to hose down our wheels afterwards.' Seeing Reg's scowl, he adds, 'For eff's sake, it's a joke!' His mate in the Harvard University T-shirt is more forthcoming. 'They was here. I saw 'em. Can't say which way they've gone,' pointing for answer at the steamed-up windows.

At the roundabout he's offered a three way choice. He takes the middle and puts pressure on the pedals, but after twenty minutes loses heart. Maybe he's on the wrong road? Just as he's about to turn back, he glimpses a cyclist approaching from the opposite direction.

The silhouette says it's Unreconstructed Ken on his 1950s Claud Butler with heavy saddlebag and low fixed gear. He must have got dropped off the back on a hill and the Wobblers have gone on, impatient to wet their whistles and expecting him to follow. He's come home early to escape their ribbing, saddlebag packed with excuses – today it's 'the grandchildren visiting'.

The two men straddle their machines at the roadside. 'So where you been,' Sarky Ken asks, 'polishing your nice new chain?' Reg recounts his clash with the Mini mob, consciously elaborating to his advantage.

'You want to watch it. Trouble's easy to find if you go looking for it. Some o' them young hooligans carry knives.'

'Knives? So what? I was taught unarmed combat fighting the Chinks in Korea. Learned how to keep my cool.'

'Oh, I'll bet you was cool as a cucumber.' Ken always has that dismissive annoying grin on his cherubic choirboy face. 'Say what you like,' Reg insists, 'one way or another if it was necessary I could've seen 'em off.'

Ken informs him the Wobblers are planning to 'indulge' at The Bell in Little Appleton and bids him farewell.

The cosy, rustic bar room smells of wood smoke from the open hearth. His mates have yet to arrive. He takes his pint up to the log fire and gulps it down quickly, so someone will see the empty and buy him a refill. And, yes, he's in luck. As he contemplates the residue of foam on the inside of his empty glass, chatter and clatter in the entrance hall announce the Wobblers' presence. His good mate Jacko, queuing at the bar, gestures with raised hand and eyebrows. Soon his second pint of Hobsons is in his hand and going down a treat.

Can life get better than this, he wonders: a couple of pints of real ale, a packet of crisps and a story to tell to a captive audience? At the crowded table, the Wobblers are all ears as he recounts the contretemps with the youths. In his mind it's fast becoming a fisherman's tale, not at all scary, but with suitable additions and omissions a magnificent adventure over which he's had full control. As his audience leans close, he somehow recalls details he'd almost forgotten: how, for example, he'd deliberately hung back to taunt his pursuers and extend their punishing run. 'I kept letting them get up close and then I'd sprint away again. I kept shouting, "Come on, lads! Don't tell me you're out of puff already?" You should've seen their faces.'

Everyone agrees their boy's done good, a credit to the Wobblers. In his place, most would've reacted the same. And wasn't it gutsy, facing down those young ruffians who might have been carrying knives. He deserves a medal, someone says, grinning broadly as he looks around and takes the others into the joke.

Knives? Come to think he did see something flash in their hands as they ran. 'Wasn't you just a bit scared?' Jacko asks, points out today's hoodlums aren't like the dear old Teddy boys with their razors. 'They just used to slash, but this lot are butchers. You can end up in the morgue.'

'Put it this way. When I was in Korea, I was taught unarmed combat. No, honest, I killed with my bare hands.' He exposes his skinny, veined wrists above the table and wrings the neck of an imaginary chicken.

That caps it for the Wobblers. They wildly applaud the Bald Bard, as someone dubs him. Whatever the truth, it's been a great story and two more pints have mysteriously materialised as Reg has been talking.

The discussion broadens to cover road rage – cyclists going about their lawful business being harassed, threatened, endangered, even killed, and how they shouldn't take it lying down anymore, unless, as Jacko jokes, they've been knocked down and don't have much choice. It's generally agreed there are too many unreasonable motorists with a downer on cyclists who, if you discount the couriers and the Mayor of London and our future Prime Minister, Dave Whatshisface, breaking the law on *their* bikes – the sentence collapses in general hilarity. Anyway, whatever, thugs should get their comeuppance.

His glass has been emptied and re-filled more times than he cares to recall before the conversation moves on. The Wobblers have ordered bar snacks, but he feels too replete and hyped up for food. 'What's it like being a hero?' Jacko asks. Well, he won't forget today in a hurry, that's for sure. Too soon, it seems, the time comes to depart.

As they near the town, one by one the Wobblers peel off to their various destinations until Reg finds himself riding alone down the High Street. With umpteen pints of Dutch courage swilling in his belly, he jumps a red light, even though now there's no emergency, as vehicles from both sides surge forwards. With the Wobblers' acclamation cloaking his shoulders, he feels he has a new lease on life. He scrapes through by a whisker. Even when he hears the sound of a vehicle pulling in behind him, he feels no concern until, with a sudden squeal of tyres, it shoots past and swings across, forcing him to stop. It's the Mini! Oh my God… he sees the long scratch over the wheel arch as the doors open. With only seconds to react, he dismounts and drags his bike over the pavement to the swing doors of a department store. Seeing no way for his bike to fit, and not thinking to upend it, he drops it at the entrance.

The compartmented glass provides only brief refuge from the youths hot on his trail. This time they must have knives. Once inside the bustling store, he doesn't look back but takes to his heels in a fast, stiff-legged hobble, weaving through racks of clothing and past open-mouthed customers and sales assistants. Some clap him, this seemingly frantic old gentleman in black tights and gaudy top, advertising Quick Step and yelping theatrically as he runs. Are they on camera? Is it a publicity stunt for some TV comedy show? Maybe Russell Brand and Jonathan Ross or some other celeb will put in an appearance?

His headlong rush takes him to the back wall. There's nowhere left to go then but through a door with a green sign – two doors. He bursts through the first one he comes to and stops dead.

'Bugger me!' A volley of barrack-room oaths tumbles from his lips.

It's a bare upended bottom with short chubby legs thrust in the air. The young woman in front of the dark green plastic tray beside the washbasins is tucking a nappy beneath a baby's tiny buttocks. The small boy on the floor playing with his toy car breaks off in alarm at this strange intruder, who looks like a clown, but utters the wicked words of a kidnapper. At once his playschool training kicks in. He points an accusatory finger and starts shouting in the squeaky little voice of an automaton, 'Stranger danger! Stranger danger!'

Reg's hand instinctively covers his face, as the woman turns to view him with terrified incomprehension. Then she starts to scream. Her mouth opens out into a huge red cavern of screaming that throbs and echoes in his ears. She tucks the baby under her arm, seizes the little wide-eyed boy's hand and, chin down, plunges past Reg and out through the exit. He can still hear her distressed cries coming from the department store as he bolts himself inside a toilet cubicle. Overcome with nausea, he bows his head over the pan and vomits up a brown mess of beer and crisps.

Only seconds later, it seems, the door bolt is rattling like a machine gun as someone hammers on the outside. An angry voice yells, 'Let's be having you, you foul-mouthed pervert, or we'll break in.'

He wipes the sick from his mouth onto his sleeve. He put his full weight against the shuddering door. 'Go 'way!' he croaks. 'For Christ's sake, go 'way!' Adding in a quivering voice, 'I'm warning you. Don't mess with me, you young devils. I'm a trained killer.' Dizzy, he sinks to the floor.

A stunned silence – then an alarm sounds. An appeal goes out over the speakers for customers to evacuate the store. The outer door to the women's toilet facilities squeaks open and shut as more security backup enters to cope with the paedophile emergency and threat of violence.

There's a hurried, whispered consultation. Someone scrabbling up the partition of the next cubicle. At the sound of boots kicking against the thin board, Reg's skinny body shakes. He sits in nauseous aftershock, hiding his head in his arms, sobbing. Something awful has happened, but how and what? The boots thud back to the floor.

'It's an old guy dressed up queer. Like some loony cross-dresser or something.'

The outer door keeps opening and shutting until he imagines the small space must be bulging with people intent on doing him harm. Another body claws up the dividing wall.

It's a woman. Reg can't comprehend exactly what she's saying to him. It's something about forget the fighting talk and behave sensibly – issues needing to be resolved. He's in trouble, but won't come to any harm if he unbolts the door and gives himself up. It's a matter of commonsense.

She talks on and on. That voice … there's something familiar about it.

He looks up, eyes half blinded with tears, heart balking at every other beat like a fence to be jumped. His head is swimming. The blurred, wavering image of a woman's face gazes down from the top of the partition. It's backlit and haloed by a ceiling light. Commonsense, the mouth repeats, commonsense – but the words seem to be coming from elsewhere, from above and beyond the room, much higher up and farther out in the ether of memory – not threatening but softly chiding.

'Mags?' he falters in confusion. 'Mags, is that you?'

*   *   *   *

Now it's months after the event and nearly all over, he doesn't give a flying-shag for the witches. Of course, it doesn't take much imagination to know Maureen and Patricia will have made a meal of the newspaper clippings. 'All that,' they'll say, 'all that waste of taxpayers' money, and what happens – he gets off with being drunk in charge of a pedal cycle and disturbing the peace. It's absolutely disgusting. All the other charges dropped – indecency, threatening behaviour and so forth, all dropped. They were even investigating him under the Terrorism Act with him saying he was a trained killer.'

And then they'll say, 'Ah, but he had a very good solicitor. Angela said so. Argued he was just a confused old man with an attitude problem. Went on about the effect on his mind of fighting in Korea. What did that have to do with it, I ask? It was years ago. And all that stuff about him missing his wife and not getting over the shock of finding her dead in bed. Poppycock! More like shock of not finding his dinner in the oven.'

And then the two broomsticks will cackle. 'It's all cost him a packet, another big chunk of her inheritance gone up in hot air. He hasn't even been sentenced yet. It says here he's been released on police bail pending a psychologist's report – which amounts to being let off scot-free. No one really believed all that nonsense about him being chased by men with knives, not even his buddy-buddies, after what happened. Of course, the CCTV was on the blink.'

'If there's one good thing to come out of all this, in Angela's opinion, it's that his bike was nicked from outside the store by somebody or other and the old fool hadn't bothered to insure it. At least, now he can't go out again with his cronies getting into mischief.'

They'll go on talking over the garden wall until they hear him slam the back door and see him carry Jacko's third best bike out into the kitchen garden. Then Maureen will scurry to the boundary fence and part the shrubbery to investigate. Then she'll call back over her shoulder, 'You're not going to believe this, Patricia. It's him. And he's got himself another bike. He's hung it up on a sort of stand. It's an old-looking, second-hand sort of thing, all scratched and battered. He's turning the pedals.'

Yes, you old witches, turning the pedals. And now he's unshipped the chain – quite deliberately with a screwdriver, sprung it off the ring. But you don't know that, do you? No, because bikes are a total mystery to you and broomsticks don't have chains.

'Oh dear!' She's calling over her shoulder. 'Something awful's happened. The chain's come off. Oh dearie me, Patricia, some people never learn. You should just hear the language.'